WHAT YOUR DOCTOR WANTS YOU TO KNOW TO

CRUSH
MEDICAL
DEBT

Virgie May-Bright Ellington
What Your Doctor Wants You to Know
222 Purchase St. #239
Rye NY 10580
info@crushmedicaldebt.com

ISBN: 979-8-9853001-0-9 (print)
ISBN: 979-8-9853001-2-3 (hardcover)
ISBN: 979-8-9853001-1-6 (ebook)
ISBN: 979-8-9853001-4-7 (audiobook)

Ordering Information:
Special discounts are available on quantity purchases by corporations, associations, and others. For details, contact info@crushmedicaldebt.com

A Health System Insider's 3 STEPS TO PROTECT YOURSELF from America's #1 Cause of Bankruptcy

WHAT YOUR DOCTOR WANTS YOU TO KNOW TO

CRUSH MEDICAL DEBT

Virgie Bright Ellington, MD

Dedicated to the survivors of COVID-19, the families of those who were not so fortunate, and all those who struggle with billions of dollars in medical bills.

DISCLAIMER

CONTENTS

PART 1:
CRUSH YOUR MEDICAL BILLS

PART 2:
CRUSH YOUR MEDICAL DEBT

PART 3:
GET HELP WHEN MEDICAL DEBT
IS CRUSHING YOU

A portion of the proceeds from the sale of this book goes to RIP Medical Debt to help Americans crush more than $1 trillion in medical bills.[1]

A portion of the proceeds from the sale of this book goes to RIP Medical Debt to help Americans crush more than $1 trillion in medical bills.[1]

INTRODUCTION

WHAT YOUR DOCTOR WANTS YOU TO KNOW ABOUT THE U.S. HEALTHCARE SYSTEM

MATTHEW'S STORY

I saw this story about Matthew, who has private medical insurance through his job as an essential worker at a senior living facility, in Kaiser Health News (KHN), an online newsletter that features people struggling with medical bills. Matthew was 25 years old when he passed out at work. He was diagnosed with viral cardiomyopathy, a type of heart failure complication from the flu. Although Matthew had insurance, he couldn't pay what he owed the hospital. The hospital sued him, and Matthew ended up filing for bankruptcy before his 30th birthday.

As Matthew told KHN, "The curse of being sick in America is a lifetime of debt (…) The biggest crime you can commit in America is being sick."

He said he "always made sure to take jobs with health insurance, so I thought I'd be all right."

But, like nearly half of Americans under age 65 with private insurance, Matthew has a high-deductible health plan with a yearly out-of-pocket maximum that's unaffordable if he has the misfortune of having a serious medical problem.

Two years after Matthew declared bankruptcy, he was told he needed a cardiac ablation, a procedure to fix complications from the cardiomyopathy. Because the ablation was elective (not an emergency), Matthew met with the hospital's representatives ahead of the scheduled procedure to set up a payment plan for the anticipated $7,000 cost, which is more than a quarter of his annual salary. Matthew is beginning to realize the $500 a month payment he agreed to is still beyond his means, and admits he's afraid he's facing another bankruptcy.[1]

MORAL OF THE STORY:
Americans are sick, tired, confused, overwhelmed, overcharged and under-covered by our healthcare system—and one serious medical illness or injury away from financial catastrophe.

My physician colleagues and I spend our days, weeks and years helping patients live healthy and well—"living right," as I call it. Taking time to learn about healthcare finances is living right, too. Many of us understand very clearly that the system is not on our side: U.S. healthcare companies and providers are not in the business of taking care of our financial health. To be honest, they can destroy our finances and devastate our future. A 2019 *American Journal of Public Health* study reports more than 60% of all U.S. bankruptcies are related to medical debt.[2]

While nonprofit and for-profit hospitals are aggressively fine-tuning their accounting systems to get patients to pay big bills and send more patient accounts to debt collectors, healthcare insurance companies have figured out how to get patients to pay higher deductibles and bigger percentages of coinsurance. We've all heard painful stories behind this heartbreaking statistic: medical bills are the #1 cause of bankruptcy in the United States.[3]

After almost 25 years as an Internal Medicine physician and more than 10 years as a health insurance executive, I've seen the U.S. medical care system provide healthy profits to everyone from every angle: providers, insurers, administrators, consultants, suppliers and vendors. Everyone profits—except the patient.

Life happens. We get sick and injured.

At the time that we're the most vulnerable—when we're weak or exhausted, when we're in pain or afraid—American patients are taken advantage of and bullied into paying large bills so that our critically ill healthcare system can profit. Don't fall for it. Don't allow it to happen to you.

As you'll see in the stories in this book, hospitals and

healthcare providers jump on the American patient first to get their charges paid—whether the patient has insurance or not, and whether or not insurance denies coverage of the services. There's a reason for this.

Have you heard the saying, "He who has the gold makes the rules"?

The U.S. healthcare system is run on the engines of insurance companies. American health insurance companies have the gold, and force hospitals and doctors to accept negotiated lower payments for their services. Patients who don't have insurance or are underinsured haven't negotiated these lower prices with providers and pay "retail"—full price—when they get the bill.

So, U.S. providers would rather get you—the patient—to pay the bill out of your pocket, because they make more money from you than from an insurance company.

MIA'S STORY

Mia is a 34-year-old mother of two young children who was my hospital roommate when I had emergency hernia repair surgery. Her husband works tons of days and hours at a 24-hour diner while she takes care of their preschool-age girls. Mia was a lot of fun. She would pretend to get electrocuted from the automated vital signs machine her nurse connected her to and tell funny stories, just to make me laugh.

During our conversations, Mia shared that this was the second time she'd been admitted in the past year for concerns she might have a stroke. I felt badly for this young, sweet mom who must be scared about her health, but I became more upset when she told me the details about paying for her first hospital stay.

As she was being discharged, a hospital representative came to her room, presented her with a bill for the admission, and demanded Mia sign an agreement that forced her to accept a payment plan that almost amounted to as much as her husband brings home in an entire year.

I explained to Mia that the most important rule when you get treated at an emergency department or hospital is to NEVER agree to a payment plan on arrival or at any point during your stay.

MORAL OF THE STORY:
NEVER sign a financial agreement or payment plan before you get the actual bill for an emergency room or hospital visit!

As I asked Mia, how can we agree to pay for services if we don't know how much and for what we're being charged? We don't receive itemized bills and the opportunity to review them for accuracy until after we get home from an ER or hospital, so you should never agree to a payment plan during the registration or discharge process.

Likely, though, if you're reading this book, you've already

needed expensive medical care, like a hospital stay. If you remember nothing else, the top two important medical money rules I want you to know are:

1. Whether or not you have insurance, don't pay any bill before you ask for and receive your itemized bill (see Chapter 1).

2. If you have insurance, never pay any bill before you get the Explanation of Benefits (EOB) (see Chapter 1).

Because U.S. health insurance companies demand discounts from hospitals, they're forced to try to make up the difference on the backs of the uninsured, the underinsured, the taxpayer, and Americans who don't know their medical financial rights. Yup, you.

American taxpayers help support the United States' diseased healthcare system.[4] You pay taxes to fund states' charity care programs, which covers medical costs for those who can't afford to pay hospitals' retail rates.

But you can do your part to stop this system from taking money from you and yours. You're reading this book. You have leverage. You can do it!

Words Your Doctor Wants You To Know About The U.S. Healthcare System

On the journey to getting your medical bills paid, you have to learn a few key words the U.S. healthcare system is counting on you not knowing.

The world of healthcare insurance uses medical and legal words that can be confusing, which leads us to a general rule: **if you don't know what something means, ALWAYS ask!** Never be intimidated to ask, and keep asking, questions until you understand what you're reading or hearing about your medical coverage and healthcare. When you encounter someone who's not willing to help, politely move on and ask someone else.

To be able to recognize the mistakes medical bills frequently contain, you have to learn enough of the language to understand the words, codes and abbreviations describing the services you're paying for.

Starting below and throughout this book, we'll go through the buzz words and definitions related to paying medical bills. You don't have to memorize the meaning of every word—just refer back to this list if you need to refresh your memory as you go through the book.

MEMBER:
Person (you or your dependent) covered by an insurance plan

PROVIDER:
Hospital, doctor or any other entity that provides medical services

INSURANCE:
Company writing the check to the provider (hospital

or doctor).

DEDUCTIBLE:

Amount you pay for all healthcare services before the insurance starts to pay.

For example, with a $1500 deductible, you pay for all the first $1500 of covered medical care.

After the deductible is met (paid) for the year, you only pay the copays and coinsurance for covered services.

COINSURANCE:

Percentage of costs for services you pay after the annual (yearly) deductible is met; you pay some and the insurance company pays some.

COPAY:

Set amount you pay toward prescriptions, outpatient and ER visits, and other healthcare services.

IN-NETWORK:

Provider (hospital or doctor) has a contract with the insurance company to accept a lower negotiated amount for its services as payment in full.

OUT-OF-NETWORK:

Provider (hospital or doctor) doesn't have a contract with the insurance company.

Some insurance plans will not pay for any services by out-of-

network hospitals and physicians, leaving you to pay for 100% of what's billed by providers who are not part of your insurance plan's network.

If you have insurance, it's important to know which type you have.

American health coverage is generally broken into two categories: commercial (private) insurance and government (Medicare or Medicaid) insurance.

Commercial (Private) Insurance

PREFERRED PROVIDER ORGANIZATIONS (PPOS):

Network of providers who contract with an insurer to provide medical care at reduced prices.

Although PPO plans often have lower copayments and deductibles when you use a network provider, there are usually bigger out-of-pocket costs than with other plan types. However, one of the benefits of PPOs is that you don't need a referral from a primary care physician to see specialists.[5]

➔ *Be careful:*

Even if you don't need a referral, certain procedures and services have to be authorized in advance (pre-authorization) by a doctor with pretty much all types of insurances. When in doubt, call your insurance company to advise them of an upcoming test or procedure and ask if it needs to be pre-authorized.

HEALTH MAINTENANCE ORGANIZATION (HMO):

Organization contracted with a restricted list of providers you can choose from or to whom your primary care physician can refer.

One of the benefits of HMOs is lower premiums and deductibles and little or no copays. However, all care and specialists must be referred by your assigned primary care physician.[6]

POINT OF SERVICE (POS):

Combination of PPO and HMO plans

As a POS plan member, you get HMO benefits when you visit HMO providers and PPO benefits when you see PPO providers.[7]

POS plans also usually have out-of-network benefits, meaning that some portion of out-of-network providers' bills are covered.

HIGH-DEDUCTIBLE HEALTH PLANS (HDHP):

Low premiums with very high deductibles; you pay lower monthly premiums but a much higher percentage of any medical services.[8]

Because these plans have relatively low premiums but deductibles in the $5,000 to $7,500 range, they're attractive to healthy young adults who rarely need to visit doctors.

High-deductible plans aren't quite as appealing if you have an accident or develop a serious illness.

SELF-INSURED:
Companies have a large fund from which healthcare services for their employees are paid.

In these cases, the company pays a commercial insurance plan to oversee payments to providers.

DISCOUNT PLANS:
For a monthly fee, you pay for participating providers' services at an alleged discount.

→ *Be careful:*
Discount plans aren't "real" insurance.[9]

Even though these plans are advertised and marketed as health insurance, you're responsible for all costs for every service: doctor visits, lab tests, x-rays and CT scans, procedures, hospitalizations and surgeries.

Government-Sponsored Insurance
(Affordable Care Act, Medicare, and Medicaid)

AFFORDABLE CARE ACT (ACA):
Commercial insurance plans regulated by the Affordable Care Act (ACA), aka "Obamacare," for those who are without healthcare coverage but don't qualify for Medicaid.

Initially, the ACA was created as insurance reform. Under the ACA, health insurance companies can no longer deny coverage of pre-existing conditions or place lifetime coverage limits for care.

The ACA also allows young adults under age 26 to be covered by a parent's health plan. And, importantly, the ACA gives you the right to appeal denials of your healthcare insurance bills.[10]

MEDICARE:

Medicare covers U.S. citizens over age 65 and with certain disabilities who don't have health insurance via an employer.

Medicare has four parts.

MEDICARE PART A

Covers inpatient care (if you get admitted to a hospital, skilled nursing home, rehab, or hospice)

→ *Be careful:*

Someone with Medicare who spends a night, or even two, in the hospital does not necessarily have their stay covered (eligible for payment by insurance) by Part A.

Crazy, right?

See Admission versus "Admission" in Chapter 1.

MEDICARE PART B

Covers outpatient services, including office visits, medical equipment needed at home and some home health services

We all contribute to the costs of our Medicare Part A coverage through our Social Security taxes. However, Part B is voluntary and requires monthly premiums for those who choose to participate. Also, Medicare Part B has an annual deductible and 20% coinsurance for Medicare-eligible services.

➔ *Be careful:*

Just because you're the right age for Medicare coverage, it doesn't mean you automatically have Medicare Part B. It's optional. You have to sign up for it.

MEDICARE PART C

Medicare Part C describes plans run by commercial insurance companies that agree to follow Medicare guidelines in exchange for a fixed payment every month.

Commonly known as Medicare Advantage, Medicare Part C plans cover Medicare Part A and Part B and, most importantly, usually the Medicare copays, coinsurance and other fees original Medicare doesn't pay like dental care, optometry services (such as exams for eyeglasses), hearing aids and screening tests.

➔ *Be careful:*

A little known fact is that original Medicare Part B has 80/20 coinsurance, which means Medicare pays for 80% of non-hospital medical bills and you pay 20%.

Also, original Medicare Part A charges you copays if you're in the hospital more than 60 days (approximately $352 per day in 2020).

MEDICARE PART D

Medicare Part D is Medicare's prescription drug plan, run by private companies.[11]

One More Thing About Medicare Coverage

There are Medicare supplemental, or Medigap, plans, which cover fees original Medicare doesn't pay, like the 20% coinsurance, for example.[12]

➡️ *Be careful:*

Some who pay for a Part D prescription plan mistakenly believe they have a Medicare supplement plan and get left with huge coinsurance bills.

Double check what type of plan you're paying for and what it covers.

MEDICAID:

Medicaid is run by each state government to provide coverage for those with low income.

Like Medicare, commercial insurance companies are paid to run Medicaid in some states.[13]

Medicaid also covers nursing home costs for those with income and assets below a certain amount.

A Tale Of Two Predators: Predatory Billing & Predatory Lending

Recently, I heard the story of a gentleman who was told he couldn't take his wife home from the hospital until he paid her bill.

The man walked to the nearest pay phone in the hospital lobby (this was back in the day before cell phones), called the local police, and told them, "The hospital is holding my wife for ransom. I want you to come down here and arrest them for kidnapping"!

The police did come to the hospital, and allegedly advised the hospital administrator that they would in fact be taken into custody if the man's wife was not released.

Many Americans are aware of predatory lenders—financial companies that charge outrageous fees and create payment plans that trap desperate borrowers into descending hell holes of insolvency.[14] Several states and a few federal consumer protection laws have been passed to protect vulnerable people against predatory lending, and it's way past time to pass laws to protect powerless patients against predatory billing. Predatory billing practices are exactly the same as those of predatory lending, only the industries are different. (See Predatory Lending versus Predatory Billing, below.)

Until our elected leaders pass laws to protect us from the U.S. healthcare system's predatory billing tactics, we have to learn how to protect ourselves.

Predatory Lending   vs   Predatory Billing

Predatory Lending	Predatory Billing
Predatory lending is any practice by a lender using deceptive, coercive, exploitative or unscrupulous tactics to convince, induce and/or assist a borrower to take out a loan they are likely not able to afford.	Predatory billing is any practice by a provider using deceptive coercive, exploitative or unscrupulous tactics to convince, induce and/or assist a patient to commit to pay a bill they are likely not able to afford.
By definition, predatory lending benefits the lender and ignores the borrower's ability to repay the debt.	By definition, predatory billing benefits the provider and ignores the patient's ability to pay the bill.
These lending tactics often take advantage of a borrower's lack of understanding about loans terms and finances.	These billing tactics often take advantage of a patient's lack of understanding about rights, terms and finances.
Predatory lenders typically target minorities, the poor, the elderly and the less educated.	Predatory billers typically target minorities, the poor, the elderly and the less educated.
They also prey on people who need immediate cash for emergencies such as paying medical bills, making a home repair or car payment.	They also prey on people who are overwhelmed with fear, confusion, pain and/or weakness due to illness or injury.
Predatory lending practices can be found at any point in the,loan-buying process, from false advertising to high-pressure sales tactics to an unaffordable fee structure or payment plan.	Predatory billing practices can be found at any point in the medical care and/or discharge process, from high-pressure paperwork signing tactics to creating an unaffordable payment plan.[15]

Same tactic, different industries.

Special Note About Healthcare Coverage For U.S. Military Veterans
Taking Care of Those Who Take Care of Us

TAYLOR'S STORY

My best friend JoAnne's brother-in-law is Taylor, a 72-year-old career Army veteran and Tennessee farmer. Although Taylor gets his healthcare at a VA medical center, he was rushed to a community hospital closer to his home one morning after losing consciousness and falling off his tractor.

Months later, JoAnne told me about a hospital bill her sister and Taylor are struggling with. Apparently, because Taylor wasn't transferred to the VA medical center after he was stabilized at the community hospital, the VA was refusing coverage of several thousands of dollars from the hospitalization.

After a year of many (many!) calls between the hospital and JoAnne's sister, the VA agreed to cover Taylor's remaining bills.

Healthcare coverage for American veterans is funded by the Veterans Administration (VA). Although active and retired military beneficiaries and their dependents were treated only at military facilities in the past, recently the VA has contracted with some community providers to care for their members.[16] This was done in an effort to give veterans more access to healthcare, as they have historically had to wait months to years (!) for appointments for basic care at VA facilities. Unfortunately, the rollout of community care options does not seem to have significantly improved veterans' healthcare access, partly due to appointment cancellations as a result of the COVID-19 pandemic.[17]

Unfortunately, off-site care for veterans by non-VA providers doesn't always get covered. For example, emergency transportation and ER visits, cancer treatment and mental health services are too frequently denied coverage. Worse, veterans' credit scores are being affected by delays in the VA reimbursing providers.[18]

We, as a nation, can do a better job of taking care of those who sacrifice so much to take care of us. One thing we can all do is support politicians who propose bills to expand the option of Medicare for all veterans who need health and dental care.

PART 1

CRUSH YOUR MEDICAL BILLS

STEP 1: FIND THE MISTAKES IN YOUR MEDICAL BILLS

Up To 90% Of Medical Bills Contain Errors[1]

Carol is a hospital nurse with private health insurance. Chemotherapy and radiation treatment for pancreatic cancer has left her exhausted, largely from trying to pay piles of medical bills.

As Carol told a reporter in 2019, "It's not any one individual. It's not any one system or provider (…) The whole system is messed up (…) There's no recourse for me except to just keep making phone calls."

"Even as a nurse, I feel like it's impossible to understand (what different bills mean)," she said. "I can't make heads or tails of (them)."[2]

Some of the errors included a $18,000 chemotherapy bill submitted by the provider to the insurance company with missing information, which was then denied because it was late. An $800 MRI bill was denied because the insurance said the provider didn't get preauthorization.

Some studies conclude that up to 90% of all medical bills contain errors. 90%! Yikes![3]

One audit showed hospital bills of $10,000 or more have an average of $1,300 of billing errors.[4] Even more concerning—but not surprising—is that these mistakes are very rarely in favor of the patient. Actually, Medicare, the federal government's medical insurance for persons over age 65, charges big penalties against insurance companies, hospitals and physicians for making billing errors. So, as you can probably guess, providers work really hard to make sure bills they send to Medicare don't have mistakes.

But the rest of us are on our own. Yup, shock and awe: U.S. insurance companies' and providers' profits from overaggressive accounting and bill processing are carried on the backs of Americans. Protect yourself and your family; arm yourself with the same tools that hospitals and other healthcare providers use to charge you for their bills.

Words Your Doctor Wants You To Know To Find Medical Bill Mistakes

CLAIM:
Bill submitted to an insurance company from a provider (hospital or doctor) for medical services provided.

EXPLANATION OF BENEFITS (EOB):
Statement from your insurance explaining what medical services have been billed by the provider, what's been paid or

not paid by the plan, how much went toward the deductible and any remaining amount you might owe to the provider.

POLICY:
Insurance plan benefits and exclusions

BENEFITS:
What you're covered for

EXCLUSIONS:
What you're not covered for

USUAL, CUSTOMARY, AND REASONABLE:
The price that insurance plans decide they'll pay for a medical service, typically based on rates other providers are charging in your area.[5]

OUT-OF-POCKET MAXIMUM:
After you've paid this specified amount in coinsurance for medical services in a given year, the plan will cover any coinsurance costs for the rest of the year.

DATE OF SERVICE (DOS):
Date an office or hospital visit was made, or a test or procedure was performed.

GLOBAL SURGICAL PACKAGE:
One charge for all care, including postoperative visits, associated with a surgical procedure.[6]

CURRENT PROCEDURAL TERMINOLOGY (CPT) CODE:

Five-digit numbers used to describe medical services and procedures.[7]

Providers use CPT codes to determine how much they're going to charge for each service; insurers use CPT codes to determine how much they're going to pay for each service.

For example, CPT code 99203 describes a new patient or outpatient visit.[8] A new patient is anyone who hasn't been seen by the doctor or another doctor of the same specialty in the same doctor group in the past three years. Because providers get paid more for a new patient than an established patient, new patient CPT codes cannot be used for an established patient visit.

HEALTHCARE COMMON PROCEDURE CODING SYSTEM (HCPCS) CODE:

Type of CPT code with five digits (letters and numbers) that describes medications, supplies, and some services.[9]

You might see HCPCS codes as part of your medical bill alongside or instead of CPT codes.

INTERNATIONAL CLASSIFICATION OF DISEASES, 10TH REVISION (ICD 10) CODE:

Four to seven-digit numbers used to describe diagnoses, symptoms and certain procedures.

Every diagnosis (condition) is represented by an ICD (International Classification of Diseases) code.[10] For example, R00.1 describes bradycardia (slow heart rate).[11]

N39.0 describes a urinary tract infection (UTI).[12]

You might see ICD 10 codes with your insurance claims or medical records.

REVENUE CODE:

Codes assigned to specific facilities (hospital or medical center), indicating where a patient's treatment took place—emergency room, operating room, or another department.[13]

You might see revenue codes as part of your medical bill alongside CPT codes.

INCIDENTAL OR UNBUNDLING:

Using more than one CPT or procedure code to bill for a service that should be billed as one code.[14]

Providers often charge for things that should be included in one charge separately. The term for this in the medical insurance world is incidental.

When procedures, operations and laboratory tests get denied by an insurance plan as incidental, it means the billed service was broken out—or unbundled—from a whole service bundle described by one medical code.

An example of a service denial as incidental to another service is an incision (surgical opening) as part of an operation. The surgical incision is incidental to (included in) the operation—the procedure cannot be performed without the incision, and therefore cannot be billed separately.

PRIOR AUTHORIZATION (AKA PRE-CERTIFICATION OR PREDETERMINATION):

Requirement by your insurance plan that your doctor gets approval from the plan before it will cover certain services, treatments, devices or medications.

➔ *Be careful:*

If the doctor obtained prior authorization, it does not guarantee payment. The plan's medical policies may determine the service is not medically necessary for the particular condition (as described by the ICD 10 code billed with the service).

HIPAA (HEALTH INSURANCE PORTABILITY AND ACCOUNTABILITY ACT):

United States federal law that gives you the right to inspect, review and receive a copy of your medical records (except psychotherapy notes) and billing records that are held by healthcare providers and health insurance companies.[15]

Note:

A provider cannot deny you a copy of your records because you have not paid for the services you have received.

However, a provider may charge for the reasonable costs for copying and mailing the records. The provider cannot charge you a fee for searching for or retrieving your records.

YOU GOT A BILL—
NOW GET THE RIGHT BILL

When we receive hospital bills, they're actually *summary* bills.

Summary hospital bills are generally one or two pages and have no CPT codes. (See Example 1a.)

What you need to have to make sure you're not being overcharged is the itemized bill. Itemized hospital bills are at least 10 or 20, maybe up to 200 pages, and have CPT codes. (See Example 1b.)

Think about it: have you ever gotten a cell phone bill or electricity bill that's just one page? No. The *first* page of phone and utility bills is a *summary* of what's owed; the next few pages break down charges by item, e.g. calls, electric, gas, fees, taxes, etc.

The Health Insurance Portability and Accountability Act of 1996 (HIPAA) is a federal law requiring all providers give patients full access to their medical records. Providers who don't fully comply with this law face severe fines and penalties.[16]

Hospitals count on you not knowing you have a legal right to an itemized bill. An itemized bill lists the services you're being charged for item by item, before you're expected to pay.

Seriously, can you imagine any other kind of business

sending us summary bills with the expectation to be paid? If grocery stores, department stores, credit card companies, etc. treated us the way American healthcare providers do, we would demand legal and political involvement and maybe even accuse them of fraud.

Call the hospital's billing or patient accounts department and ask for an itemized bill **with CPT codes.** Unfortunately, many hospitals that change their prices depending on who's paying aren't willing to give you a bill with CPT codes. Representatives in these facilities may tell you they don't have that information, make excuses as to why they don't have that information and/or can't give it to you, or say things like, "That's information we can only give an insurance company," or "You'll have to call your insurance company to get that information," or "That's claim information. We don't have that here."

When you run into cases where a facility isn't forthcoming with giving you your itemized bill with CPT codes, politely ask to speak with a supervisor and say you're making a request for your "complete itemized bill with CPT codes as per HIPAA medical records access requirements."

If you have continued difficulty, put the request for an itemized bill with CPT codes in writing. In the letter, give them a deadline with a date to respond by and let them know you'll file a HIPAA violation complaint with the Office of Civil Rights (ocrportal.hhs.gov) if you haven't received it.

```
    DETAIL SUMMARY                              SVC FAC:  WOKC      11/16/20  0936
                                                                          DIV CD: W
 PT NO:                                                                  ACCT TYPE: O
 REG: 10/25/20  DSCH:              FC: X  PT: G  EXP IND:   ACCT BAL       83570.38
 -------------------------------------------------------------------------PAGE NO:   1
    TOTAL CHARGES:        83570.38                    NURSE STA/ROOM:        /
       ACCT BAL        X03  V      B01  V                                      PT BAL
       83570.38     83570.38         .00                                         .00

     LINE    DEPARTMENT            TOTAL AMT          INS BAL             PT BAL
 !    1     PHARMACY                  25.00            25.00               0.00
 !    2     MEDICAL SUPPLIE         3538.38          3538.38               0.00
 !    3     LABORATORY             2418.00          2418.00               0.00
 !    4     PATHOLOGY                391.00           391.00               0.00
 !    5     OPERATING ROOM        38440.00         38440.00               0.00
 !    6     ANESTHESIA             1035.00          1035.00               0.00
 !    7     DRUGS/MEDICATIO         377.00           377.00               0.00
 !    8     RECOVERY ROOM          4046.00          4046.00               0.00
 !    9     TRTMNT/OBSERVAT       33300.00         33300.00               0.00
 ---------------------------------------------------------------------------------
  ! (PF14) SEL PT                             KEY IN LINE NO __ AND PRESS ENTER
  ! (PF15) RETURN TO PT OVERVIEW                           PF16 D/E  ____

 PAQCHS01
```

Example 1a: Summary bill – No CPT codes

Statement of Hospital Services
Statement Date: 11/17/20

Page 3 of 4

Guarantor:

Yale
NewHaven
Health

Hospital Services Provided - Itemized Charges, Adjustments & Payments *(continued)*

Patient Name:
Service Date(s): 07/31/20 - 08/01/20
Location:

Primary Insurance:
Secondary Insurance:
Patient Class: Outpatient

Service Date	Revenue Code	HCPCS/CPT Code	Description Of Hospital Services	Quantity	Amount
07/31/20	0250	J3490	ROCURONIUM 10 MG/ML SOLN	7	$98.29
07/31/20	0250	J3490	SODIUM CHLORIDE 0.9% PF 0.9 % SOLN 10 ML VIAL	20	$3.70
07/31/20	0250	J3490	D5 1/2 NS WITH KCL 20 MEQ/L 20 MEQ/L SOLP	1	$10.00
07/31/20	0270		Hc Oxygen Hours	2	$74.20
07/31/20	0270		PACK ROBOTIC	1	$269.46
07/31/20	0270		BALLOON KII BLUNT TIP 12X130MM	1	$297.40
07/31/20	0270		TROCAR KII BALLOON 12X100MM	1	$297.40
07/31/20	0270		SCISSOR METZENBAUM JAW INSERT 5MM 31CM	1	$215.37
07/31/20	0270		TRAY FOLEY METER 16FR	1	$54.78
07/31/20	0270		Hc Robotic Supplies	1	$3,831.15
07/31/20	0300	81025	Hc Urine Pregnancy Visual	1	$65.00
07/31/20	0300	87086	Hc Culture, Bacterial; Quantitative Colo	1	$63.00
07/31/20	0300	81001	Hc Urinalysis Auto W/micro	1	$33.00
07/31/20	0310	88307	Hc Pathology V Complete - Technical	1	$685.00
07/31/20	0360		Hc Operating Room Minute Level 3	105	$25,846.80
07/31/20	0370		Hc Anesthesia Per Min	109	$3,753.96
07/31/20	0636	J7120	LACTATED RINGERS SOLP	1	$5.00
07/31/20	0636	J2704	PROPOFOL - INJECTION 10 MG/ML EMUL	20	$10.70
07/31/20	0636	J2704	PROPOFOL - INJECTION 10 MG/ML EMUL	72	$38.42
07/31/20	0636	J2001	LIDOCAINE 20 MG/ML (2 %) SOLN	10	$12.70
07/31/20	0636	J0690	CEFAZOLIN 1 GRAM SOLR	4	$9.57
07/31/20	0636	J2250	MIDAZOLAM (PF) 1 MG/ML SOLN	2	$2.54
07/31/20	0636	J0131	ACETAMINOPHEN 10 MG/ML SOLN	100	$141.50
07/31/20	0636	J3490	SUGAMMADEX 100 MG/ML SOLN	2	$347.83
07/31/20	0636	J1885	KETOROLAC 30 MG/ML (1 ML) SOLN	2	$22.00
07/31/20	0636	J1100	DEXAMETHASONE 4 MG/ML SOLN	4	$11.12
07/31/20	0636	J3010	FENTANYL PF 50 MCG/ML SOLN	1	$2.65
07/31/20	0636	J1170	HYDROMORPHONE PF 2 MG/ML SOLN	1	$1.10
07/31/20	0636	J7120	LACTATED RINGERS SOLP	1	$5.00
07/31/20	0636	J2405	ONDANSETHON (PF) 4 MG/2 ML SOLN	4	$5.21
07/31/20	0636	J2175	MEPERIDINE PF 50 MG/ML SOLN 1 ML VIAL	1	$2.45
07/31/20	0636	J1644	HEPARIN (PORCINE) 5,000 UNIT/ML SOLN	5	$3.72
07/31/20	0710		Hc Recovery Room Per Minute	112	$3,403.68
08/01/20	0300	85025	Hc Bl Count Cbc Auto W/auto Diff	1	$90.00
08/01/20	0300	36415	HC COLL OF VENOUS BL BY VENIPUNCT	1	$23.00
08/01/20	0636	J1644	HEPARIN (PORCINE) 5,000 UNIT/ML SOLN	5	$6.13
					$39,654.36

Total Charges:

continued on next page

Example 1b: Itemized bill with CPT codes

ONE HOSPITAL VISIT—A *BUNCH* OF BILLS!

What *Is* This?

When you have an operation or a hospital stay, you're almost always going to get multiple bills for the same visit.[17] At minimum, you get two bills: one from the hospital and another from the doctor group(s) who treated you.

Other separate charges you might get:

- ER doctor
- Hospitalist (doctor who treats you while you're in the hospital)
- Plastic surgeon
- Pathologist (doctor who looks at your biopsy or tissue and laboratory results)
- Radiologist (doctor who reads your x-ray, CT scan, MRI and other imaging studies)
- Facility fee
- Laboratory fee
- Radiology fee

Use these tips to help keep bills organized:

1. Keep all bills for the same procedure or hospitalization together.

2. Highlight on each bill who it's from so you can easily refer to it if more bills come in.

3. Don't throw out any bill, even if it looks like a duplicate.

   Read it thoroughly to ensure it's not a bill from another entity, like a doctor group or a laboratory.

4. Make sure you are not billed twice for the same procedure by two separate entities.

   For example, you get a hospital bill with a charge for laboratory fees. You should not get a bill from the laboratory for the same fees on the same date of service (DOS).

5. If you're disputing a charge, double check which facility or service provider the charge is from.

If You Have Insurance, Match The EOB Against The Itemized Bills

When we have private insurance covering our medical bills, the first notice we get of what we've been charged for our care is an Explanation of Benefits (EOB). This document often says, "This is not a bill." (See Example 2.)

You may have to sign up on your insurance company's website to get your EOB if the company has gone paperless.

After you receive the itemized bill with CPT codes you

requested, compare it to the EOB.

- Make sure each service described is correct, including the date of service (DOS).

- Read which services were considered covered versus not covered.

- Check how much the plan considered "reasonable and customary" payment for each covered service.

- Watch your deductible: Look at how much of the annual deductible has been met and/or went toward each covered service. Insurance companies sometimes incorrectly charge you after you've met your annual deductible. Save every bill you pay and keep an eye out for charges above your deductible.

If you have Medicare, the Medicare Summary Notices you get every three months is basically the same thing as an EOB. Match Medicare Summary Notices you get against the itemized bills with CPT codes. (See Example 3.)

EmblemHealth

PO Box 2814, New York, NY 10116-2814

09/14/2020

WE WELCOME YOUR CALL

If you have any questions that this summary doesn't answer, please call us at **1-800-624-2414**, with your subscriber ID number. For other helpful information, visit us online at **www.emblemhealth.com**, where you can elect to go paperless.

Electronic Service Requested

ՈւիվիՈիՈւտեւնԱՈւնիվիդկկՈւնՈիկՈԱկՈւնիդ

56195

SUBSCRIBER NAME:

SUBSCRIBER ID NUMBER:

YOUR COVERAGE IS UNDERWRITTEN BY: GHI

SEE ENCLOSED INFORMATION ON APPEALING A CLAIM DECISION.

Health Plan Payment Summary

THIS IS NOT A BILL. Your health care provider may bill you directly for any amount that you owe.

Summary of Claims		
Amount billed	$442.00	This is the amount your health care provider billed for services.
Amount allowed	$268.91	The maximum amount we pay under your plan.
Copay	$35.00	This is the fixed dollar amount you pay when you visit a health care provider.
What my plan paid	$223.91	This is the amount EmblemHealth paid toward the bill.

PLEASE SEE CLAIM DETAILS ON THE FOLLOWING PAGES.

Year-to-Date Information for Calendar Year/Plan Year/Policy Year				
	IN NETWORK			
This Amount is Out of Pocket Amount	**Amount**	**Total**	**Annual Maximum**	**Remainder**
Individual Max Out of Pocket	$35.00	$175.00	$4,550.00	$4,375.00
Family Max Out of Pocket	$35.00	$555.00	$9,100.00	$8,545.00

IMPORTANT MESSAGE

This statement reflects services and items provided by your participating provider. You are responsible for services that are not covered by your benefit plan, such as charges for non-covered days or services and for any applicable copayment, coinsurance and/or deductible. A service that has been denied due to inadequate information, or because prior approval was not obtained, is the responsibility of the provider and **you do not need to take action.**

We know you're busy. Here's a quicker, more convenient and secure way to receive your Explanations of Benefits: Go Paperless! Whenever we process a claim for you, we will send you an email letting you know you can view it in your secure personal page of emblemhealth.com. Just register at emblemhealth.com and choose "Go Paperless".

Group Health Incorporated (GHI), Health Insurance Plan of Greater New York (HIP), HIP Insurance Company of New York and EmblemHealth Services Company, LLC are EmblemHealth companies. EmblemHealth Services Company, LLC provides administrative services to the EmblemHealth companies.

Example 2: Explanation of Benefits (EOB) summary page

09/14/2020

Health Plan Payment Detail

Service Date	Claim Number Type of Service Provider	Amount Billed	Amount Allowed	I Owe or May Have Paid	My Plan Paid	Notes
07/20/20	.45200 EVALUATION/MANAGEMENT, 99214 ✳	$332.00	$223.03	Deductible $0.00 Coinsurance $0.00 Copay $15.00	$208.03	
07/20/20	15200 DIAGNOSTIC, OFFICE 93000 ✳	$110.00	$35.88	Deductible $0.00 Coinsurance $0.00 Copay $20.00	$15.88	

✳ CPT CODE

Group Health Incorporated (GHI), Health Insurance Plan of Greater New York (HIP), HIP Insurance Company of New York and EmblemHealth Services Company, LLC are EmblemHealth companies. EmblemHealth Services Company, LLC provides administrative services to the EmblemHealth companies.

Example 2: Explanation of Benefits (EOB) itemization of services

Medicare Summary Notice
for Part B (Medical Insurance)

463650499
Page 1 of 4

The Official Summary of Your Medicare Claims from the Centers for Medicare & Medicaid Services

THIS IS NOT A BILL

Notice for

Medicare Number	XXX-XX-ᵕ
Date of This Notice	**August 10, 2018**
Claims Processed Between	**May 18 – August 10, 2018**

Your Deductible Status

Your deductible is what you must pay for most health services before Medicare begins to pay.

Part B Deductible: You have now met your **$183.00** deductible for 2018.

Be Informed!

Medicare has started mailing new Medicare cards to everyone with Medicare. You don't need to do anything to get your new card. Medicare will mail your new card to the address you have on file with Social Security. Visit Medicare.gov/newcard to learn more.

Your Claims & Costs This Period

Did Medicare Approve All Services?	**YES**
See page 2 for how to double-check this notice.	
Total You May Be Billed	**$21.87**

Providers with Claims This Period

April 2, 2018
Inpatient Consultants MI PC

¿Sabia que puede recibir este aviso y otro tipo de ayuda de Medicare en español? Llame y hable con un agente en español.
如果需要国语帮助，请拨电话和医疗保位，请先说 "agent"，然后说 "Mandarin"   **1-800-MEDICARE (1-800-633-4227**

Example 3: Medicare Summary Notice (MSN) summary page

Your Claims for Part B (Medical Insurance)

Part B Medical Insurance helps pay for doctors' services, diagnostic tests, ambulance services, and other health care services.

Definitions of Columns

Service Approved?: This column tells you if Medicare covered the service.

Amount Provider Charged: This is your provider's fee for this service.

Medicare-Approved Amount: This is the amount a provider can be paid for a Medicare service. It may be less than the actual amount the provider charged.

Your provider has agreed to accept this amount as full payment for covered services. Medicare usually pays 80% of the Medicare-approved amount.

Amount Medicare Paid: This is the amount Medicare paid your provider. This is usually 80% of the Medicare-approved amount.

Maximum You May Be Billed: This is the total amount the provider is allowed to bill you and can include a deductible, coinsurance, and other charges not covered. If you have Medicare Supplement Insurance (Medigap policy) or other insurance, it may pay all or part of this amount.

April 02, 2018
Inpatient Consultants MI PC, (810)220-5222
PO Box 844906, Los Angeles, CA 90084-4906

Service Provided & Billing Code	Service Approved?	Amount Provider Charged	Medicare-Approved Amount	Amount Medicare Paid	Maximum You May Be Billed	See Notes Below
Subsequent hospital inpatient care, typically 35 minutes per day (99233-GV) ※	Yes	$275.00	$109.36	$85.74	$21.87	A,B
Total for Claim #	~ 430	$275.00	$109.36	$85.74	**$21.87**	

※ CPT CODE

Notes for Claims Above

A The approved amount is based on a special payment method.

B After your deductible and coinsurance were applied, the amount Medicare paid was reduced due to Federal, State and local rules.

Example 3: Medicare Summary Notice (MSN) itemization of services

CRACK THE CPT CODE

....

Look at the Code Description & Make Sure It Matches the Services You Received

Many medical bill mistakes are due to charging the wrong CPT code for a service.[18] CPT codes are assigned by the American Medical Association (AMA). Every medical service (test, visit, procedure or operation) has a specific CPT code. For example, 58572 describes a hysterectomy.

Think of CPT codes as bar codes for medical services. Just like bar codes attached to each product in a store, providers attach a price to every CPT code.

Cracking the CPT code is the most critical step to not overpay for medical care.

When you receive your itemized medical bill with CPT codes that you requested, Google each CPT code to find the code's description.

For example, a Google search for CPT code 99218 will bring up multiple versions of the definition. Look for a description that has the most detail. One of the first descriptions that comes up on the search for code 99218 is *"an initial Observation Care CPT code (99218 - 99220) should be reported for patients admitted and discharged from observation status for less than 8 hours on a calendar date"* (UnitedHealthcare).[19] This sounds like a lot of what I call "medical-ese"—very technical language that's not so easy to understand.

Do some scrolling to find a detailed description that sounds more like plain English. Eventually, you'll find this definition for code 99218: "Initial observation care, per day, for the evaluation and management of a patient (…) Usually, the problem(s) requiring admission to outpatient hospital "observation status" are of low severity. Typically, 30 minutes are spent at the bedside and on the patient's hospital floor or unit."[20]

In my experience, the most detailed code description helps make it easier to read and more understandable.

CPT Medical Coding

CPT codes are organized into categories corresponding to the human body.

- Anesthesia (00100-01999)
- Surgery (10021-19499)
- Musculoskeletal (20005-29999)
- Respiratory System (30000-32999)
- Cardiovascular System (33010-37799)
- Digestive System (40490-49999)
- Urinary System (50010-53899)
- Male Genital System (54000-55899)
- Female Genital System (56405-58999)

- Nervous System (61000-64999)

- Eye and Ocular Adnexa (65091-68899)

- Radiology/Diagnostic Radiology (70010-79999)

- Pathology and Laboratory (80047-89398)

- Medicine, Special Services, Procedures and Reports (90281-99607)

- Evaluation and Management (99201-99499).[21]

Now that you've cracked the code, you're ready to…

CATCH COMMON MEDICAL BILL MISTAKES

The most common errors in medical billing are clerical errors:

Basically, typos and wrong codes entered into the chart, invoice or EOB.[22]

For example, if your date of birth (DOB) or gender is mistyped, an insurance computer will automatically deny some services. The system will automatically deny covering a service if it reads that you're too young for a screening mammogram, for example.

Other common mistakes:

Your wrist sprain is accidentally coded as a wrist fracture. Or the hospital billed the code for a brand-name drug when you took the generic version.

One big mistake that outpatient providers frequently make is to charge patients who have insurance for preventive care services. By federal law (the Affordable Care Act, aka ACA or Obamacare), insurance companies must cover age-appropriate preventive care services, such as screening mammograms and screenings for Type 2 diabetes, cervical cancer and colorectal cancer, without charging copayment or coinsurance. This is true even if you haven't met your annual deductible.

Unfortunately, many providers aggressively get around this law by "creative" coding. For example, a woman who has been treated for breast cancer in the past might be told her yearly routine "screening" mammogram is actually a "diagnostic" mammogram, and therefore not eligible for the free benefit. Check out www.crushmedicaldebt.com for important tips on how to battle and win against this preventive care billing problem.

Common mistakes that cause insurance companies to deny your claims:

- No-preauthorization for a medical service. Many expensive tests, medications, procedures or treatments require the provider to get advance approval from the insurance.

- Incidental medical services unbundled from a larger service. Unbundling is a way of double charging for a service that's already included in another charge. Hospitals often charge for services and items that should be included in the room charge.

For example, air compression stockings used on the day of surgery should be included in the "facility fee." Extra supplies like gloves and facial tissues should be considered as part of the daily room fee.

(See also Words Your Doctor Wants You to Know to Find Medical Bill Mistakes at the beginning of this chapter).

- Some codes can't be billed with other codes. For example, codes describing procedures, like S0630, can't be billed with codes for office visits. The provider can bill a code for the office visit (like 99201), or the procedure (S0630), but not both. If both codes for the same day are submitted to insurance, they will automatically get denied for payment.

- Certain procedure codes can only be billed with certain disease codes. For example, a pacemaker procedure (like 33208, which is insertion of new or replacement of permanent pacemaker) can only be billed with certain heart disease codes (like R00.1, which represents bradycardia or slow heart rate). If the only ICD code submitted to insurance with procedure code 33208 is for hypertension (high blood pressure), the procedure code will automatically get denied for payment.

- Certain procedure codes can't be billed together. For example, code 58551, which describes uterine fibroid removal, can't be billed with a hysterectomy (removal of the uterus). It's not reasonable that a fibroid, which is attached to the uterus, is being removed if the entire uterus is removed during the same operation.

- Duplicate or multiple billing for the same service on the same date.

Common mistakes in hospital billing:

- A super common error that hospitals make is double or multiple billing (charging for the same service more than once).

- Another common mistake is wrong quantities. A typo can easily get you charged for 100 tablets of a medication instead of 10.

- Check that you're charged for the correct length of stay (LOS) and the right type of room.

  For example, be sure you weren't charged for the day of discharge, which is not allowed by most insurance plans. Also, if you had a shared room, look to make sure you're not billed for a private room.

Common mistakes in outpatient billing:

- Make sure all outpatient copays you paid have been

applied to your account. This is probably the most common mistake in outpatient visits.

- Ask for your medical records from the provider and check the office notes. An office note typically documents symptoms (chief complaint), the doctor's exam or findings, and the plan for treatment and any recommended follow up.

- Double check that all billed CPT codes match procedures documented in the notes. It's never appropriate to bill for a service not clearly written in the office notes.

- Most importantly, for all outpatient visits, make sure you haven't been charged for a 30-minute visit code (for example, +99203 if you're a new patient) when the doctor was only with you for 10 minutes (99201).

BRUCE'S STORY

My husband, Bruce, struggled with shoulder pain for almost a year before he got it looked at by an orthopedic surgeon. The orthopedist diagnosed shoulder tendonitis and referred him to physical therapy (PT) for treatment.

I was happily surprised at how well Bruce's pain responded to PT, and he finished the prescribed PT sessions after about 6 to 9 months. A few months after his last session, Bruce got a bill from the PT provider for more than $400. When we looked at the bill closely, it didn't take us long to figure out that none of *the copays Bruce had paid at the beginning of every visit had been applied to his account.*

Ugh.

Bruce fixed the problem and got the bill resolved with one call to the physical therapist.

- Like all outpatient services, make sure all copays are applied to your PT/OT visits.

- Watch the number of PT/OT visits you make. Most plans limit the number of PT/OT visits in a year, but you may have been told by your provider that you need more than the annual limit to get back to functioning normally.

Common mistakes in medical equipment billing:

- Home health agencies and pharmacies sometimes charge rental fees for devices like wheelchairs or infusion pumps. Go through their bills to make sure you're not getting charged beyond what the equipment costs to buy. Medicare and commercial insurance won't pay more than the actual costs of equipment—you shouldn't either.

Common mistakes in surgery billing:

- Pay attention to which surgeon is billing you for your operations. Often, surgeons have assistant surgeons or co-surgeons working with them in bigger procedures, and they bill separately from the primary surgeon. Even though Medicare and commercial insurance plans insist that assistant surgeons bill less than 20% of the primary surgeon's charge,[23] the assistant surgeon will often bill a price close to the same amount as the primary surgeon.[24] If you don't catch and fight these inappropriate charges, you're the one stuck paying a higher coinsurance—or, if you don't have insurance, the entire bill. (See Izzy's Story, Step 3.)

- Double check the operating room time. Request your medical records and compare the time on the anesthesiologist's records with the hospital's bill to make sure you're not billed for more time than was actually used.

Common mistakes in radiology (X-rays, CT scans, MRIs, etc.) billing:

- According to the American College of Radiology, in order for you to be billed for X-rays, CT scans, MRIs, etc., a report must be given that contains all of the following:

  » Type of imaging exam

  » Indication (reason for doing the exam)

  » Description of the exam and technique used

  » Findings (results)

  » Conclusion (and recommendations, if needed)

> » Signature of physician performing and reading the imaging exam[25]

Be sure all of the above is included in each imaging report you're being charged for. If not, you should not be billed for the service.

Common mistakes in ER billing:

In my experience as a medical insurance executive, bills for ER services are some of the most likely to include mistakes and, therefore, one of the most frequently denied by insurance. This means it's one of the most common medical bills many Americans can't afford to pay.

- Like office visits, make sure the description of what's billed is accurate. Specifically, be sure the severity of services being charged match the level of services you received.

For example, ProPublica, an online investigative journalism newsroom, shares a story about a couple in Houston, Texas overcharged by an ER facility after having their 8-year-old son tested for COVID-19.

A couple of weeks after the ER visit, the couple received a bill from the facility for almost $2,500. The couple, who has private insurance through a taxpayer-funded state employee plan, contacted the ER billing department and asked for an itemized bill. The charge for the COVID-19 test was $175. The rest of the bill was for a facility fee of $1,784 and a physician fee of $486 for a CPT code 99283 Emergency department visit Level 3.

If you do an online search for CPT code 99283, the definition is an emergency visit and evaluation that includes an "expanded problem focused history and physical examination" and "medical decision making of moderate complexity."

In this case, the visit took less than five minutes total. While the child stayed in the car, his vital signs were taken, but no physical examination had been performed. "You're getting a drive-thru test, and they're pretending like they're giving you emergency services," the child's mom said.[26]

Common mistakes in ambulance billing:

- Make sure the billed code describes emergency transportation—not just a very expensive ride to the ER.

For example, CPT code A0428 (*Ambulance service, basic life support, non-emergency transport*) and A0426 (*Ambulance service, advanced life support, non-emergency transport*) represents non-emergency transportation,[27] and will always get denied by insurance.

If you had to be taken to the ER by ambulance for emergency medical care, call the ambulance service directly to request the codes to be corrected to CPT code A0429 (*Ambulance service, basic life support, emergency transport*) or A0427 (*Ambulance service, advanced life support, emergency transport*).

For example, if you end up in an ER that doesn't have the level or type of care you need and have to be transported to a second facility by ambulance, the CPT code should be A0429 or A0427.[28] (See Janine's story, Step 2).

Putting It All Together—You Can Do This!

- You got your itemized bills with CPT codes.
- You Googled CPT codes to understand what was billed.
- You found the common mistakes in your medical bills.

Now that you've found the mistakes in your medical bills, you have the info you need to fix the mistakes in your medical bills.

YES!

STEP 2: FIX THE MISTAKES IN YOUR MEDICAL BILLS

JANINE'S STORY

Janine, my best friend's daughter, has done really well managing the Type 1 diabetes she was diagnosed with at the age of 2. She had been able to dodge diabetic ketoacidosis (DKA), a dreaded diabetes complication, until one night a couple of weeks before senior prom. Janine's mom called an ambulance to get her to the nearest emergency department as fast as possible, which was fortunate: the doctors in the ICU where Janine was admitted said she was dangerously close to having brain damage from the DKA episode. We felt really grateful when Janine came home happy and healthy a few days later.

A year later, Janine's mom received a bill from the ambulance provider for $2,400(!) and asked me to take a look at it. When I looked at the bill, the ambulance ride was coded as "non-emergent." Non-emergent services are always the patient's responsibility. They're never covered by insurance.

I advised Janine's mom to call the ambulance service to point out the error. She got a profuse apology from the customer service rep who answered the phone and was told to disregard the bill.

Janine's mom never heard from the ambulance provider again. And she saved $2,400.

MORAL OF THE STORY:
Have the mistakes in your medical bills fixed by those responsible for making them!

Words Your Doctor Wants You To Know To Fix Medical Bill Mistakes

OBSERVATION:

Care for six to 24 or more hours to determine if you need to be officially admitted to the hospital.

Even if you spend a night–or two(!)–in the hospital, your status is still observation unless a treating doctor wrote an order for admission.

You might not know whether or not you're still in observation status after two nights in the hospital unless you're told by a doctor or the hospital administration staff.

ADMISSION:

You're officially admitted into a hospital or facility, usually with the expectation you're going to be there for more than two nights.

INPATIENT:

Medical services received while officially admitted to a hospital.

OUTPATIENT:
Medical services received outside of an official hospital admission.

CONTACT YOUR PROVIDER TO FIX MEDICAL BILL MISTAKES

Start a battle journal—a notebook to document your work.

Reach out to the provider's billing or patient accounts department to discuss the mistakes you found in the itemized bill with CPT codes. Be kind and patient with everyone you speak to and write down the date, time, representatives' names, and outcome of every interaction.

Some mistakes to look for and bring to a provider's attention requires requesting your medical records:

- ER care is one of the most frequent medical services that get miscoded by the provider's billers. Make sure the description of what's billed matches the level of services you received. (See Common Mistakes in ER Billing, Step 1.)

- Radiology (X-ray, CT, MRI scans, etc.) services frequently get denied by insurance because of incomplete provider documentation, including:

  » The provider did not document the medical necessity for the test.

> » The treating physician did not sign the order or requisition.[29]

Look for these in the orders section of your medical records.

- Drug screening tests are often denied for the same reasons as radiology services. You would also find these in the orders section of your medical records.

- For those on Medicare, providers are required to provide all patients with an Advanced Beneficiary Notice of Non-Coverage (ABN) to sign before treatment. This document means the patient is aware they're financially responsible for any services that are not covered by Medicare.

If you're challenging a bill that includes a service not covered by Medicare, request your medical records and look for a signed ABN.

If you didn't sign it, you don't owe it.

DOCUMENT ALL CONVERSATIONS

Remember to keep the tone with everyone you speak to friendly and non-confrontational. It really is true: we catch more flies with honey than with vinegar. Being nice gets us better service. Also, keep in mind the person on the other end often wants to help, and if they can't, it's because they haven't been trained well enough to be able to be helpful.

When you run into hospital, provider and/or insurance reps who aren't giving you the information you need, politely ask to speak to a supervisor for assistance.

Your goal in every conversation is to ask the representative to help you get the information you need. Make hospital, provider and insurance reps your friend, not your enemy.

But be persistent! It may take months or years(!) to reach a deal you can afford with hospitals and providers but keep it up. It's really worth it to keep going. Look at it this way: if you're contesting a $27,000 hospital bill and it takes you two years to get it reduced to $1,000, you just made $13,000 a year—that's a pretty decent part-time job!

ADMISSION VERSUS "ADMISSION"

Be aware: just because you stayed over for a couple of nights in the hospital, it doesn't mean you had a hospital admission.[30] For example, if you go to the ER for chest pain, you may end up staying for a night or two for tests to make sure you're not having a heart attack or another serious problem.

This is considered "observation," not an official "admission" to the hospital. Why is this important? Because traditional Medicare and many private insurance plans cover hospital services differently than other care. Like, charging 20% coinsurance for everything not part of a hospital admission kind of different. For an "observation" stay of two days and nights in the hospital getting evaluated for chest pain, you're looking at being on the hook for $5,000—20% coinsurance of a $25,000 bill. Big difference!

So, keep in mind:

Staying in the hospital more than 48 hours = admission.

Staying in the hospital less than 48 hours = outpatient observation.

If you're challenging a hospital bill from a stay that was approximately 48 hours, talk with the patient accounts supervisor to make sure the visit is documented as an admission, not an observation.

SHOULD YOU HAVE QUALIFIED FOR FINANCIAL HELP FOR YOUR MEDICAL CARE?

In exchange for non-profit tax status by the U.S. government, non-profit hospitals have to show they support those in financial hardship.[31] This includes taking care of persons who don't have insurance coverage and can't afford to pay for their medical care out-of-pocket. These accounts are often referred to as financial assistance or charity care.

The problem is many hospitals don't appropriately screen

patients for eligibility for charity care, financial aid, or Medicaid, which means when these accounts go unpaid, they get inappropriately sent to collections. One medical debt industry insider reports more than 30% of accounts sent to bill collectors should have qualified for charity care.[32]

Demonstrating the same problem, a study done by Congress in 2006 found many hospitals don't inform patients charity care is available.[33]

If you're struggling at all with being able to afford a bill, call the hospital patient accounts department, and request and submit a financial assistance application.

Putting It All Together—You're One Step Closer!

- You started a battle journal.
- You called the provider to fix mistakes you found in Step 1.
- You checked to see if you should have qualified for financial help.

HAPPY DANCE!

STEP 3: FIX THE MISTAKES IN YOUR INSURANCE COVERAGE

DONNA'S STORY

Donna has "really good" private health insurance through her job at a large bank. So, she was surprised when the insurance company notified her it wasn't covering a $500 MRI ordered as part of her annual breast screening.

This year, Donna thought an area where she had a biopsy in the past felt unusual, which she brought to the mammogram team's attention. After taking pictures with the mammogram, an ultrasound was done, and then an MRI was performed to try to get a clearer look at the area. The radiologist (physician specializing in taking pictures of the body with machines like x-rays and CT scans) read the MRI as a "probably benign (not cancerous) mass."

Three months later, Donna got an EOB (Explanation of Benefits) from her insurance stating the breast MRI was not paid because it was "experimental and investigational." "Experimental and investigational" is a fancy way of saying a medical service is not medically necessary. When she called the plan to figure out why the test ordered by the mammogram provider (radiologist) was denied coverage due to being experimental and investigational, Donna was told the insurance's clinical policy (statement of what they cover versus not) says MRIs are not necessary in situations like hers.

Donna brought the MRI denial to the attention of the radiologist and asked for help in appealing the insurance company's decision. The mammogram provider wrote a letter pointing out the insurance's mistake: Donna's situation actually matched one of the company clinical policy reasons for doing an MRI.

Several weeks after getting the radiologist's help with her appeal, Donna received a letter stating the denial was overturned (the disputed service was allowed and paid by the insurance).

MORAL OF THE STORY:
Mistakes happen, but don't let erroneous insurance denials cost you.

WHAT TO DO WHEN YOUR INSURANCE WON'T COVER YOUR MEDICAL BILL

Humans make mistakes, especially in the complicated medical and health insurance world. The millions of medical bills and claims processed by insurance companies every month are handled by humans and computer systems programmed by humans, making the likelihood of errors almost a given. **Always contest insurance claim denials!**

Be on the lookout for insurance denial mistakes because they have serious (meaning, expensive!) consequences. If there's anything in your EOB you don't understand, call the plan and ask for help with an explanation. It's imperative to always appeal services denied by insurance. **We always pay much (much!) more for denied services!**

- Providers—especially hospitals—expect you to pay *full price* for non-covered (denied) services.

- You're going to end up paying more than your insurance policy's promised yearly "out-of-pocket maximum."

For example, let's say you're being treated for cancer with chemotherapy. The provider charges $3,500 for each treatment. If your insurance agrees to cover the chemotherapy, they will only pay the doctor at the rate considered "reasonable and customary," which is usually *not* the entire $3,500. However, if the particular chemotherapy recommended by your doctor is considered "not medically necessary" or "experimental and investigational" by your plan, the provider might send you a bill—and expect payment—for the entire $3,500!

Also, because the insurance is not covering the treatment, the costs for the chemotherapy is not included in the out-of-pocket maximum limit stated in your plan policy benefits. This means you're on the hook for the *entire charge*, even if you've met your out-of-pocket maximum for the year.

So, you can see how **denials of medical care by your insurance can add up to a lifetime of debt and/or bankruptcy–fast!** If we don't challenge erroneous insurance denials, we're at serious risk of paying more for our healthcare than the yearly out-of-pocket maximum stated in our insurance plan benefits. Out-of-pocket maximums only apply to bills or parts of bills our insurance plan *agrees* to cover. Any claim (bill) denial is money that comes out of our pockets—no matter what the plan says about its out-of-pocket maximum limit policy.

Words Your Doctor Wants You To Know To Fix Insurance Mistakes

BALANCE-BILLING:
In-network provider charges you for the difference between the amount they bill and what your insurance pays.

For example, if a provider who is in your insurance plan's network (accepts your insurance) charges $100 for a service for which your insurance plan pays $10, the provider has signed a contract with the insurance company to accept the $10 as payment in full. Billing you for the balance—the remaining $90—is balance-billing and in violation of the contract the provider signed with your insurance company.

SURPRISE-BILLING:
Out-of-network providers working at your in-network

facility charge you for the difference between the amount they bill and what your insurance pays.

For example, let's say you're seriously injured and get transported to the emergency department of your in-network hospital for care. Often, hospitals contract with emergency room physicians, radiologists, pathologists or anesthesiologists who don't participate in insurance plans to provide services in their facilities. So, if these providers charge $3,000 for a service but your insurance plan would consider payment of $300 for the service as usual and customary, the providers will send you a bill for the remaining $2,700—if you have out-of-network benefits. If you don't have out-of-network benefits, they're expecting you to pay the whole $3,000.

CLINICAL POLICY:

What an insurance company covers or doesn't cover for testing or treatment of a specific condition, disease, illness or injury.

NOT MEDICALLY NECESSARY:

When something doesn't meet accepted medical standards to diagnose or treat a disease, illness, injury or symptoms.

EXPERIMENTAL AND INVESTIGATIONAL:

A fancy way of saying not medically necessary.

Usually, a service denied as experimental and investigational has not been determined as being 'the standard of care' for a condition in well-known medical studies.

FORMULARY:

List of medicines covered (allowed) by insurance plans.

Why Most Americans Are One Accident Or Illness Away From Financial Disaster

IZZY'S STORY

Izzy is a 21-year-old college student covered by her mother's insurance. Izzy's parents double-checked to make sure the hospital and surgeons doing the repair of the knee meniscus she tore playing tennis was in-network with their insurance plan.

The hospital charged Izzy's insurance more than $96,000 for the surgery but accepted $3,000 from the insurance company and a co-pay of $300 from her parents as payment in full. Yikes… This is a great example of the outrageous difference between what medical providers charge insurance plans versus those of us without an insurance company's bargaining power. If Izzy's parents didn't have insurance, they would've been on the hook for the entire charge of $96,000 instead of a $300 co-pay! Because the insurance company can leverage their bargaining power, they're charged only $3,000 while you, the individual, are expected to pay $96,000 for the same service.

Then, Izzy's parents got a bill for more than $1,000 from the assistant surgeon in her operation. Because this provider was out-of-network, the plan denied coverage for his services, leaving them on the hook for the entire bill.[34]

BRAD'S STORY

Brad is a dentist from Austin, Texas who broke his hip in a freak bicycle accident. He gave his insurance information, a plan he bought through the Affordable Care Act (ACA or also known as Obamacare) marketplace, to the paramedics in the ambulance and again to the ER where he was taken.

Brad's accident left him with an emergency hip fracture repair surgery, three days in the hospital—and a bill for more than $70,000 because all the providers were out-of-network for his insurance plan.

The hospital and the insurance company were both adamant that the bill was Brad's responsibility. After weeks and weeks of trying to work it out on his own, Brad got frustrated and hired a lawyer to help him negotiate with the hospital. Eventually, the lawyer was able to get the bill down to below $3,000.[35]

MORAL OF IZZY AND BRAD'S STORIES:

This is where good folks with good insurance get into trouble. **Most Americans are just one accident or illness away from a lifetime of debt.** Super scary statistics show Americans with health insurance can be as susceptible to going bankrupt as those without insurance because of surprise billing and insufficient coverage. A study by *The American Journal of Medicine* found that most Americans who filed for healthcare-related bankruptcy in 2007 were middle-class and had health insurance.[36] A 2019 study by *The American Journal of Public Health* found that health-related bankruptcies actually increased slightly after the implementation of the ACA.[37]

Surprise billing happens when an out-of-network provider is involved in a patient's care without their knowledge. For example, you make sure you go to a hospital that accepts your insurance, but the ER doctor who treated you for a life-threatening emergency doesn't. You get sent a bill for much more—even up to tens to hundreds of thousands of dollars more—than your plan pays. The hospital or physician expects you, the patient, who may not have even been conscious at the time you received care, to pay the balance of the bill that was not covered by your insurance.

A Brookings study showed more than 20% of ER visits are provided by out-of-network providers, which puts you at risk for surprise billing.[38]

Although a few states have passed laws preventing hospitals and other providers from surprise billing, until now there was no federal law protecting Americans from getting outrageously billed when we're at our most vulnerable.

Good news: as of January 2022, surprise billing is illegal!

In the biggest U.S. healthcare system move since the Affordable Care Act, Congress agreed to ban surprise medical bills in December 2020.[39] Instead of charging patients, providers have to work out their payment disputes directly with insurance companies to settle on a fair price. The law applies to doctors, hospitals and air ambulances, but not ground ambulances.

> ➔ *Be careful:*
>
> *Until the surprise billing law goes into effect, many facilities, especially those providing ER and urgent care, ask patients to sign an agreement to take responsibility for all charges not covered by their insurance plan. If you've signed this kind of document, the facilities may make you believe you've signed away your rights to contest surprise billing. Please know you can—and should—challenge the bill as discussed later in this chapter.*

American patients are at highest risk of getting surprise bills from providers we can't choose, like:

- Emergency departments and doctors
- Ground ambulances
- Air ambulances
- Laboratory services
- Radiologists
- Anesthesiologists

NO ONE IS IMMUNE FROM BEING OVER-BILLED

VIRGIE'S STORY

Six months after a two-day stay at a regional medical center for emergency surgery, I received a bill for more than $351,000 for the "OR services" (see Example 4). It stated that "insurance payments" and "adjustments" amounted to more than $263,000, leaving a patient amount due of almost $88,000.

Obviously, this provider didn't know it was trying to pull one over on the author of What Your Doctor Wants You to Know to Crush Medical Debt. I was able to stop laughing just long enough to call my best friend, JoAnne, to tell her about the bill. She said, "Virgie, you're the only one I know who laughs when the rest of us would be curled up in a ball crying."

The medical center is an in-network provider with my insurance, which means that balance-billing me is breach of contract.

When I called my insurance company to find out how much was actually billed and paid for the services, it turns out the medical center sent the exact same "amount due" to me and my insurance! This means the medical center billed me for the same $88,000 they billed the insurance company for, despite being in-network. When I called the medical center's billing department to hear what they had to say, the rep I spoke with said, "I can't tell you how much your insurance was billed or what they paid; you're going to have to contact your insurance *company for that information. But, $88,000 is a lot of money. You certainly can't be expected to pay that all at once. You can set up a payment plan. Can I connect you with someone on our team to help you set up a payment plan?" I responded, "No, thank you. I'm good." I knew I wasn't responsible for any of that bill.*

This provider's billing practice is to try to trick patients with in-network insurance into paying balance-bill money they don't owe. Kind of like double-dipping. Playing both sides against the middle. Just all kinds of ways wrong. Breach of contract wrong. Some might even say contract fraud wrong. Wrong, wrong.

MORAL OF THE STORY:
Always, always, always challenge balance bills!

Protect yourself from being over-billed. Check all medical bills with your insurance to determine whether or not the billing provider is in your plan's network. If the provider is in-network, it has contracted to accept the insurance plan's negotiated amount as payment in full (not including any applicable deductible, coinsurance or copays) and is not allowed to bill you for the remaining balance.

Special note about ACA plans:

Depending on the state and the commercial insurance company, patients with ACA plans are either responsible for all denied medical bills like private insurance, or can't be balance-billed at all, like Medicaid patients.

WMC Health | **WMCHealth Physicians**
Advanced Physician Services
Westchester Medical Center Health Network

PO BOX 49 | ATTN: APS | PITTSBURGH, PA 15230-0049

STATEMENT

ℹ️ For billing questions, please call:
1-833-353-8886
8:30AM - 4:30 PM EST

Addressee   Page 1 of 1

VIRGIE BRIGHTELLINGTON

IF PAYING BY CREDIT CARD FILL OUT BELOW

CHECK CARD USING FOR PAYMENT ☐ ☐ ☐ VISA ☐

| CARD NUMBER | | EXP. DATE |
| SIGNATURE | | |

Statement Number	Due Date	Amount Due	Amount Paid
	04/30/2021	$87,916.00	$

Please make checks payable and remit to:

WMC ADVANCED PHYSICIAN SERVICES
PO BOX 5046
CLIENT NUMBER 400004
NEW BRITAIN, CONNECTICUT 06050-5046

☐ Check if address/insurance changes are on back

Please detach and return top portion with payment.

Statement Number	Account Name	Statement Date	Due Date
	VIRGIE BRIGHTELLINGTON	04/09/2021	04/30/2021

Date	Service Description	Charges	Payments/Adjustments	Patient Balance
	Date of Service (10/25/20 - 10/27/20) VIRGIE BRIGHTELLINGTON *Encounter #:*			
10/25/2020	88304 AP Bill Surgical Pathology Level III Complexity	$44.00		
10/26/2020	OR SERVICES	$351,664.00		
	Patient Balance			$0.00

MESSAGES
Thank you for choosing WMCHealthcare. The balance due is your responsibility.

Total Charges: $351,708.00
Insurance Payments/Adjustments: -$263,792.00
Patient Payments/Adjustments: $0.00

AMOUNT DUE: **$87,916.00**

Example 4: Balance-Billing

CONTACT YOUR INSURANCE PLAN
TO FIX MEDICAL BILL MISTAKES

First…

Find out why the service was denied. Determine the *type* of denial.

Believe it or not, some insurance denials are legitimate. However, some are due to insurance plan error. The most common reasons insurance companies deny claims (bills) include:

- Out-of-network services
- Not medically necessary or experimental and investigational services

We talked about why it's important to challenge balance billing. It's just as important to dispute "not medically necessary" and "experimental and investigational" denials. Like Donna's story at the beginning of this chapter, these denials are insurance computer system or employee mistakes way too often.

Next…

Know your rights. Learn about your benefits coverage.

Wouldn't it be nice if stress caused by trying to figure out your benefits was covered by your insurance plan? It's challenging to understand our medical bills and insurance

Explanation of Benefits (EOB). But to know your rights and what you're covered for and what you're not, you have to carefully study your insurance policy.

Minus any coinsurance and/or deductible, insurance plans guarantee to pay for *approved* medical charges— not all medical charges.

For example, if you have a commercial plan with 20% coinsurance, this doesn't mean the plan will pay for 80% of all your bills. It means the plan will pay for 80% of the "usual and customary" price of *approved* or allowed medical services.

Also...

Read your policy.

If you have healthcare insurance, you have to understand your plan benefits. To understand your plan benefits, you have to read your policy.

Read your policy. The *whole* thing, from beginning to end.

It's 'bout as much fun as watchin' paint dry and almost as painful as getting a bad tooth pulled, but if you have medical insurance, it's a critical part of not overpaying medical bills.

Pay special attention to:

- What your plan pays (benefits)
- What your plan does not pay (exclusions)

- How much the annual (yearly) deductible is
- How much the coinsurance is
- How much the copays are
- How much, if at all, the plan covers out-of-network services
- Whether there is an out-of-pocket maximum
- How much physical therapy the plan might pay for

Now you're ready to learn…

HOW TO APPEAL INSURANCE DENIALS

It's easiest to call the insurance company at the number on the back of your card to correct the mistakes you've found. In some cases, though, the customer service representative(s) you speak with will advise you that the denied service(s) can only be corrected by a formal appeal.

How to Appeal Commercial Insurance Denials

Within two months of the date you receive a notice from your plan that your claim has been denied:

1. Get the Explanation of Benefits (EOB) and find the service or item you're appealing.
2. Circle the service(s) or item(s) you disagree with.
3. Get backup.

Ask your provider to submit an explanation saying why they disagree with the decision.

Providers, especially your doctors, want to help you get their bills paid by your insurance and will work with you. Call your physician's office and ask to speak with the manager or biller. Your doctors are going to be able to submit what's called a "provider appeal," which is usually the first step to formally request your insurers to reconsider the denial of the doctor's services. Each insurance company has its own unique requirements to submit an appeal. Because physician office managers and billers work with these companies all day every day, they're best equipped to help file an appeal for you correctly.

4. Make a copy to keep for your records.

5. Make a second copy and send to the address on the EOB.

Sometimes insurance plans offer a two-step appeal: a "provider" appeal, and then, if the denial is upheld (the denied service is still not going to be paid), a "member" appeal:

- Briefly write out the problem (the denied service) and that you've asked once already without success.

- Most importantly, ask your doctor to re-phrase the explanation stating why they disagree with the decision. (Sometimes stating your case in a different way can make a big difference.)

- Send a copy of the original or first appeal and any possibly related information to the address indicated in the decision letter.

If your insurance is through your job, sometimes your employer can help.

There are large companies that will assist or even intervene in cases of denials for medical services. Some very large companies that self-insure have a representative employed by the insurance plan to work with you regarding disputes. Ask your HR department for the contact information of the company's representative with the plan. Call and email the representative to request assistance with your denial.

If your appeal to the insurance company is denied, appeal to an Independent or External Review Organization (IRO or ERO).

An external reviewer will either uphold your insurer's denial or overturn and allow the service in your favor. Insurance companies in all states are required by law to accept the external reviewer's decision.

You have to file a written request for an external review within 4 months from the date you receive a notice or final determination from your insurance that your claim has been denied.

Look at the information on your Explanation of Benefits (EOB) or on the final denial of the internal appeal by your health plan. It'll give you the contact information for the organization that will handle your external review.

How to Appeal Medicare Denials

Medicare requires you to file appeals within 4 months from the date you get the Medicare Summary Notice.

1. Get the Medicare Summary Notice (MSN) and find the service or item you're appealing.
2. Circle the service(s) or item(s) with which you disagree.
3. Write an explanation why you disagree.
4. Write your name, phone number and Medicare number on the MSN and sign it.
5. Make a copy to keep for your records.
6. Make a second copy and send it to the company on the MSN that handles bills for Medicare.

If your Medicare appeal is not successful, your case gets automatically forwarded to an Independent Review Entity (IRE).

If your IRE appeal is denied, the next level of appeal is to the Office of Medicare Hearings and Appeals (OHMA).

Your final opportunity to appeal a Medicare coverage denial is to file a lawsuit in Federal District Court. You may need an attorney for this. Check your local Bar Association for pro bono (free) services available in your area.

Putting It All Together—You're Doing This!

- You challenged balance-billing and surprise billing.

- You contacted your plan to correct insurance mistakes.

- You appealed insurance denials.

AWESOMMMME!

PART 2:

CRUSH YOUR MEDICAL DEBT

TIFFANY'S STORY

Tiffany is a California real estate agent and mom of two with private insurance purchased from the ACA marketplace (Obamacare). Her insurance plan requires a 30% coinsurance for surgeries. When she was told she needed uterine polyps removed, she looked at different inpatient and outpatient facilities to figure out which location would be most reasonable. A medical center in Poway, California quoted Tiffany a coinsurance amount of only 20% if she had the operation at that hospital.

The morning of the procedure, as she sat filling out forms in the waiting room, the hospital staff asked Tiffany for her credit card and told her she had to pay in full before the surgery. This was news to Tiffany: she wasn't told she needed to pay on the day of the surgery when she spoke to the hospital representative who gave her the quote of the operation cost. Her card was charged the amount of 20% coinsurance she had been quoted.

Several weeks later, Tiffany received a bill for the remaining 10% of the 30% coinsurance for the surgery. When she called the hospital to ask why she was being billed for the additional amount, she never got a straight answer. She made multiple calls to follow up on the problem with no budge from the hospital. Finally, Tiffany "got tired and said, 'I don't want to play this game anymore. If you want to send (this bill) to collections, you can do it, but I'm not going to pay for it.'"

Tiffany got a call several weeks later from a collection company offering to cut the remaining bill by 25% if she paid that day. Even though she could afford it, she refused. Out of principle, Tiffany knew the medical center gave her wrong information to get her and her surgeon's business and decided to fight the facility on behalf of others who don't have the time, money or energy to do so.

Eventually, Tiffany's case came to the attention of a reporter, who called the hospital. A staff member apologized for "giving the mistaken impression that (she) was getting a discount."

[Note: This was important for the hospital to state on record. Giving discounts on coinsurance or copays is illegal and in breach of contract with the insurance company, so they were essentially committing fraud.]

Because the hospital saw in their phone records that a staffer had quoted Tiffany the wrong coinsurance amount, a representative agreed to send her a statement showing the bill has been paid in full.[1]

Don't Pay Any Bills Until All Insurance Issues Are Resolved

THERE ARE TWO MORALS OF TIFFANY'S STORY:

One, always advocate for yourself.

And two, never pay medical bills until all insurance questions have been addressed.

Although Tiffany had the resources to pay the bill she was disputing, too many Americans aren't as fortunate and have claimed bankruptcy because of provider billing and insurance errors.

ALL MEDICAL BILLS ARE NEGOTIABLE

All bills are negotiable! Always negotiate a lower bill and make sure you get an interest-free payment plan.

American healthcare providers are trapped in a system where artificially high prices are created to be able to give "discounts" to insurance plans that sign contracts with them (become in-network). Patients who are out-of-network or without insurance coverage are left to pay the entire amount or whatever they can negotiate after they get the bill. Hospitals know it's unethical to charge you more than what they charge insurance companies, but they also know it's not against the law.

→ *Be careful:*
When you're in the process of negotiating with the provider, make every effort not to formally acknowledge the debt in order to preserve your potential rights in case you don't come to a mutually acceptable agreement. For example, don't sign any document that states you owe a specific amount until you get a number from the provider with which you're comfortable.

STOP PAYING THE RETAIL STICKER PRICE FOR YOUR MEDICAL CARE

Most of us know to never pay the sticker price—MSRP (manufacturer suggested retail price)—for a new car. The same thing applies to your medical care! In the claims I've reviewed over the years, providers, particularly hospitals, bill those of us without health insurance an average of 300% to 500% more than what Medicare and commercial insurance plans pay.

Go online and look up how much Medicare pays for each CPT code on your bill. These are the prices that you're going to ask the hospital billing department to reduce the charges to.

Consider Filing For Medicaid For Bills Up To Six Months Old

Low-income qualifications are different from state to state, but if you qualify in your state, Medicaid may pay for all of the bills you've already received, up to three to six months after the date of service. Submit a Medicaid application as soon as possible.

Even if you don't qualify, your child(ren) might. Look into applying to your state's medical coverage plan for children.

APPLY FOR FINANCIAL HELP FOR MEDICAL BILLS CAUSING YOU HARDSHIP

One statistic says 30% of all accounts sent to collections by hospitals should have qualified for charity care or financial aid.[2] This is a huge number of folks who didn't know they qualify for financial aid and weren't offered charity care coverage for their treatment. Some of these patients have gotten sued and their wages garnished, without ever hearing about charity care. If paying the bill(s) will cause you and your family hardship, contact the hospital billing department and ask how to apply for their financial aid program. Every hospital system has one—even for-profit facilities.

Speaking of hardship...

Only Pay What You Can Afford

Studies show most people experience hardship when their medical expenses are 3% or more of their income.[3] Figure out how much 3% of your income is and try not to pay more than that on medical bills. For example, if you get paid $500 a week, that works out to $2,000 a month or $24,000 a year. Multiply 3% by $24,000 (0.03 x 24,000), which is $720. Work out a payment plan with the provider in which you pay no more than $720 a year.

Even if you're getting calls from bill collectors, always remember you control which bills and how much you pay. Don't let anyone force you to pay a medical bill instead of taking medications as prescribed by your doctors, seeing and following up with your doctors, paying your mortgage, rent, electricity or gas, or keeping up maintenance on your car to get to and from work safely.

ALWAYS DO THIS & SAVE THOUSANDS!

If you're told your income is too high to qualify for Medicaid or hospital financial aid, consider asking the billing department for a deep discount if you pay right away. You could say something like, "If I pay 30% right now, will you write off the rest?" Investopedia.com reports that this strategy can work because the provider saves time and money if they don't have to spend months or years chasing you for payment.[4]

If you have the resources, another idea is to ask for a 25% discount off the total bill if you make a large down payment and plan to pay the remainder with an interest-free payment plan.

At the end of the day, most of us don't have tens of thousands of dollars lying around to be able to pay off a big bill. Again, please remember to **always ask the provider to give you the lower price Medicare pays.**

- **Google what Medicare pays for the services (CPT codes) you received.**
- **Call the billing department.**
- **Offer to pay the Medicare rate.**

Medicare prices may be tens of thousands of dollars less than providers' retail (sticker) prices but, as they say, a little bit of something is better than all of nothing. Paying Medicare rates for medical care may mean the difference between being able to make regular payments versus having to claim bankruptcy.

Also, whether or not you get an agreement for a lower bill, **always ask for an interest-free payment plan that fits your budget.** Whatever payment agreement you get, make sure it's put in writing and sent to you for your records.

Once all services have been billed and insurance applied correctly, and you've contacted the provider to make an interest-free payment plan you can afford…

Never Put Payments On Credit Cards, Take Out Loans Or Sell Your Home To Pay Medical Bills

Many Americans feel embarrassed when they have medical debt, and don't understand that they didn't do anything wrong and it's not their fault they can't pay medical bills.

So, we tend to rush to get rid of medical bills by transferring what we owe hospitals and providers to credit cards, thinking we can more easily pay them off over time this way.

This causes two problems:

1. High-interest credit card rates grows the debt out of control very quickly, which makes it much harder to pay off.
2. When you put medical debt on a credit card, you lose the special legal protections you're given for medical debt.

Federal laws block credit bureaus from putting medical debt on your credit report unless it's been past due for 6 months.[5] Also, any medical debt reported to credit bureaus is weighted differently than credit card debt, so medical debt is not as damaging to your credit score. And, most importantly, once you put the hospital bill on a credit card, the hospital has no incentive to negotiate with you for a lower bill or more financially comfortable payment plan.

I'm not telling you to ignore your medical bills. Just please remember that transferring medical bills to bank and personal loans, payday loans and/or credit cards is not the answer. Also, don't take money from your retirement accounts; they're protected from bankruptcy by federal law.[6]

Medical debt isn't as urgent as your other bills. Pay your mortgage, car payments and credit cards first: prioritize protecting your home, your ability to get to and from work and paying off high-interest debt.

Talk with the billing department to work out an interest-free payment plan you can afford. By the way, payment plans with a hospital do not show up on your credit report. And never miss that payment!

WHAT TO DO IF YOUR MEDICAL BILL IS SENT TO COLLECTIONS

Unfortunately, our medical bills can be sent to collections *even if we're making payments on them.* The ACA states patients of nonprofit hospitals are supposed to be given time to apply for financial assistance before "extraordinary collection measures" are taken.[7] But any outstanding balance is at risk to be sent to collections at any time.

If you're not paying the bill because you're appealing a denial from your insurance, write a letter to the provider explaining the situation and ask them to put your account on hold.

Usually, the hospital will agree to do so for 30 to 90 days.

If your bill is sent to collections, don't panic. First, ascertain if you have signed a financial agreement that obliges you to pay. The collections agency has the responsibility to validate the bill with the provider. Without a signed financial agreement, it will be difficult for the collections agency to validate the debt. Collections agencies cannot enforce the collection of debt without validating the debt.

If you do have a signed financial agreement, consult with an attorney. There are many reasons signed financial agreements may be determined invalid. For example, agreements signed under duress are generally considered to be invalid. If you signed a financial agreement together with consent-to-treat forms in a medical emergency, it might be considered legally invalid. Please consult an attorney for accurate legal advice.

CAN YOU WRITE OFF YOUR MEDICAL BILLS FROM YOUR TAXES?

If you spent a huge amount on medical expenses in a given year, speak with a professional tax preparer to see if you can deduct some of the money you spent that year.

As of 2021, you can deduct medical expenses that are more than 7.5% of your adjusted gross income (AGI).[8] For example, let's say one year you have an AGI of $100,000 and you spent $25,000 in medical expenses. Your deductible medical expenses would be $17,500 ($25,000 minus $7,500 [7.5% of $100,000 AGI]). You would be able to write off $17,500 from your taxes for that year.

Caring For A Family Member?

You Might Be Able To Write Off Those Bills, Too

If you provide care for a parent, spouse or adult child(ren) with disabilities, you know how expensive being a caregiver can be. The IRS requires a lot less money to write off these expenses than writing off our own personal medical bills. As of 2020, working caregivers can receive a tax credit for 30% of medical expenses more than $2,000 if used to help a family member.[9] Speak with a tax professional to see if this applies to you.

Submit Any Out-Of-Network Bills

Insurance companies can pay an out-of-network provider claim (bill) up to seven years after the date of service. Think back to any bills you didn't bother to submit to your plan because they're out-of-network and you might have assumed they weren't going to get covered (paid). Submit them anyway. Or have GetBetter.co, an online service, do it for you.

HOW TO GET YOUR COVID-19 BILLS PAID

TIMOTHY'S STORY

Timothy's story is another featured in KHN's Bill of the Month. He's a Colorado dad who works for a construction company with private medical insurance through his wife's job at a nonprofit organization. Timothy tried to do everything right when he developed COVID-19 symptoms at the beginning of the pandemic in March 2020. He called a nurse hotline first, was directed to go to an urgent care facility, and from there was sent to an ER.

Timothy was not tested for COVID-19 in the ER because he wasn't admitted to the hospital and was not a high-risk individual with a condition such as diabetes, asthma or heart disease, for whom providers were reserving the limited tests at that time.

A few weeks after being sent home with treatment for bronchitis, Timothy received a $3,200 bill from the ER. Although Congress passed legislation in mid-March 2020 requiring insurance companies to cover all costs related to COVID-19 testing services, there's a gigantic loophole that is leaving millions of Americans facing even bigger bills. The law requires insurers to waive all patient fees, copays and coinsurance when a COVID-19 test is performed. Because the providers seeing Timothy in the ER did not order a test, his insurance company is passing on all charges from the visit to him.

Making the problem of unaffordable COVID-19 testing bills much worse, many patients are told to go to hospital ERs, which is the most expensive place to get care. So, when insurance companies say they cover all costs related to testing for a COVID-19 diagnosis, many of their members who go to get a test but aren't given one are looking at potential financial catastrophe. Insurers are applying more than $3,000 worth of non-COVID-19 tests—instead of a $100 COVID-19 test—to yearly deductibles.

Timothy submitted an appeal for the ER bill to his insurance company, stating that because he presented during the public health emergency with symptoms possibly consistent with COVID-19 but, through no fault of his own, only received testing for similar illnesses, the fees should be waived. He said he never heard back until a KHN reporter called the company about his case a couple of months later. A hospital representative later called him with an apology and a notice that his entire bill was covered.[10]

MORAL OF THE STORY:

Insurance companies' computer systems are programmed to look for COVID-19 related diagnosis codes to waive patient charges.

At the beginning of the COVID-19 pandemic, insurance companies and the federal government tried to help struggling Americans, including waiving out-of-pocket charges for testing and treatment and reimbursing hospitals that treat uninsured patients.

The problem is, not all sick patients with symptoms were tested for COVID-19, because tests had been in short supply early in the pandemic and throughout many parts of the country.

Without the correct COVID-19 CPT and ICD 10 billing codes in the claims submitted by the provider who evaluated and treated your COVID-19 symptoms, your care may not get covered by your insurance plan. Insurance companies are directing their members to reach out to them and/or appeal a claim if they suspect a mistake.

If you feel you or a loved one has been wrongly billed for care related to COVID-19, bring it to the attention of your insurance company and hospital, urgent care facility or physician's office where you received services.

To further create confusion about who's responsible for paying for COVID-19 tests—the patient or insurance companies—the government has said insurance plans only have to waive patient out-of-pocket costs for "medically appropriate tests." The problem is, the guidelines don't clearly say which tests are considered medically appropriate. So, who do you think providers are going to try to stick with the bill?

Because the U.S. government told insurance plans to waive patient costs for COVID-19 testing to make sure everyone had access to care, many ERs and urgent care facilities aren't sending bills to Americans for COVID-19 testing beyond what their insurance plans cover—meaning, they're not balance-billing. But what about those of us who don't have insurance? Again, uninsured patients are stuck with a *humongous* bill.

Fortunately, the COVID-19 Claims Reimbursement to Health Care Providers and Facilities for Testing, Treatment, and Vaccine Administration for the Uninsured Program was created in 2020 by bipartisan federal law.[11]

Providers and facilities who have conducted COVID-19 testing of uninsured individuals, provided treatment to uninsured individuals with a COVID-19 primary diagnosis or administered an authorized COVID-19 vaccine to uninsured individuals on or after February 4, 2020 can request payment through the program and will be reimbursed at Medicare rates.

If you received a bill for COVID-19 testing, COVID-19 treatment or COVID-19 vaccination while you were uninsured, ask the provider to submit the claim to the COVID-19 Claims Reimbursement to Health Care Providers and Facilities for Testing, Treatment, and Vaccine Administration for the Uninsured Program.

Putting It All Together—You Did It!

- You made sure all bills and claims are accurate (found and fixed mistakes in Steps 1, 2 and 3).

- You negotiated charges down to Medicare rates.
- You arranged an interest-free payment plan.

WOOHOOOOOOO! 😊

PART 3

GET HELP WHEN MEDICAL DEBT IS CRUSHING YOU

If you're not able to complete the steps to paying medical bills, consider getting help.

Our healthcare system forces Americans to negotiate with Borg-sized mega-corporations for tens to hundreds of thousands of dollars out of our pocket, at a time when we're most vulnerable and therefore the least able to. Don't suffer in silence. You're not alone. Get help.

MEDICAL BILLING ADVOCACY SERVICES

A medical billing advocate can negotiate with providers and insurance companies for you to keep you from paying what you don't owe. Medical billing advocates are nurses, social workers, lawyers and healthcare administrators who can go through your medical records, compare them against your itemized bills and work out a payment plan. They usually charge a flat fee or a percentage of what they save you. This may be a good option if you have complex medical bills from several or long hospital stays or serious injury or illness. (See Resources.)

However, avoid companies and "advocates" who try to get you to take out loans to pay medical bills. Loans are in the best interest of bank administrators, loan companies and hospitals—not you.

CONTACT YOUR STATE'S DEPARTMENT OF HEALTH, DEPARTMENT OF INSURANCE, OR ATTORNEY GENERAL

STACEY'S STORY

Stacey, an Austin, Texas, first-grade teacher with private insurance, struggled for months with a $7,000 surprise bill after a hypoglycemic event landed her in an out-of-network ER. After being told by the facility she didn't qualify for financial assistance, she found out about the Texas Department of Insurance's Mediation Program. Within weeks, a mediator from the program scheduled a call with the hospital and Stacey's insurance company.[1]

You'd be surprised how quickly errors get corrected when

you get state departments involved.

For disputes with providers, like balance-billing or surprise billing, in which you get no or an unsatisfactory response, call your state department of health.

For insurance coverage disputes, find the name, address and email of your state Commissioner of Insurance and forward your case to its executive counsel. And copy in the insurance company or call them to let them know what you're doing.

Commercial health insurance companies are regulated in every state, and some states are super-aggressive in getting insurers to pay for wrongfully denied services. A few states even make insurance companies pay extra interest fees to the patient as a penalty.

MEDIA CAMPAIGNS WORK!

STACEY'S STORY CONTINUED

Before the state department of insurance mediator's scheduled call with the hospital and Stacey's insurance company, an NPR local radio reporter contacted the hospital to comment on the case. Very shortly after, Stacey said the hospital called and told her she no longer owed anything on the bill.[2]

IZZY'S STORY CONTINUED

Do you remember Izzy's story about getting surprise billed by a provider for knee surgery? It turns out Izzy's dad went to Kaiser Health News about her case. After KHN reached out to the insurance company, the insurer overturned the out-of-network coverage denial and agreed to pay the provider's fee. What's extra interesting is, although the bill should have been applied to Izzy's parents' annual out-of-pocket deductible, the insurance company never sent them any of the provider's final bill.[3]

You may have noticed a common theme among the successful resolution of several stories in this book. When providers and insurers ignore requests for help resolving problems with a medical bill, many folks go to the media.

Hospitals, medical centers and insurance companies don't like stories about financial bullying and mistreatment of their patients hitting social media or local or national news. Just saying.

RIP MEDICAL DEBT

According to the authors of End Medical Debt, more than 50% of Americans have at least two out of three criteria their charity, *RIP Medical Debt*, uses to determine debt forgiveness: low earnings, zero net worth and/or high out-of-pocket medical expenses when compared to income.[4]

RIP Medical Debt helps people, families and veterans across the U.S. avoid bankruptcy by using donations to buy and forgive medical debt from collections agencies.

Although RIP Medical Debt doesn't take individual applications, ripmedicaldebt.org has a resource list of organizations that may be able to help with your specific case.

TO LOOK UP CPT (PROCEDURE) AND ICD (DIAGNOSIS) CODES:

Free sources to look up CPT codes are becoming rare; sites that used to let you do a free search now charge membership fees.

In addition to Google, a couple of sites where you can plug in codes to get descriptions for free at the time of publication are as follows:

Findacode.com

ICD10data.com

MDSave.com

TO FIND MEDICAL BILLING ADVOCATES:

Alliance of Claims Assistance Professionals (claims.org)

American Society of Certified Medical Billing Advocates

(ascmba.org)

National Association of Healthcare Advocacy Consultants (nahac.com)

FREE GUIDE:

What Your Doctor Wants You to Know Before Paying any Medical Bill!

Go to crushmedicaldebt.com/checklist to download your free MEDICAL BILL CHECKLIST.

REFERENCES

[1] Forbes, "Americans Near $1 Trillion in Total Medical Debt," YouTube video, October 19, 2021, https://www.youtube.com/watch?v=GzmWhS-B4eU.

Introduction: What Your Doctor Wants You To Know About The U.s. Healthcare System

[1] Laura Ungar, "Heartbreaking Bills, Lawsuit and Bankruptcy – Even with Insurance," Kaiser Health News, September 25, 2020, https://khn.org/news/heartbreaking-bills-lawsuit-and-bankruptcy-even-with-insurance/.

[2] David Himmelstein, Robert Lawless, Deborah Thorne, Pamela Foohey, Steffie Woolhandler, "Medical Bankruptcy: Still Common Despite the Affordable Care Act," American Journal of Public Health 109 (3) (February 2019), https://www.doi.org/10.2105/AJPH.2018.304901.

[3] Bill Fay, "What is Predatory Lending?" Debt.org, accessed October 6, 2021, https://www.debt.org/credit/predatory-lending/.

[4] Maureen Groppe, "Who pays when someone without insurance shows up in the ER?" USA Today, updated July 13, 2017, https://www.usatoday.com/story/news/politics/2017/07/03/who-pays-when-someone-without-insurance-shows-up-er/445756001/.

[5] "HMO vs. PPO plans – what are the differences?" Kaiser Permanente Thrive, July 1, 2019, https://thrive.kaiserpermanente.org/thrive-together/health-care-101/hmo-vs-ppo-advantages.

[6] Ibid.

[7] Julia Kagan, "Point-of-Service Plan (POS)," Investopedia, updated March 7, 2021, https://www.investopedia.com/terms/p/pointofservice-plan-pos.asp.

[8] "High Deductible Health Plan (HDHP)," HealthCare.gov, accessed October 25, 2021, https://www.healthcare.gov/glossary/high-deductible-health-plan/.

[9] "Medical discount plan," Health Insurance.org, accessed October 25, 2021, https://www.healthinsurance.org/glossary/medical-discount-plan/.

[10] Will Kenton, "Affordable Care Act (ACA)," Investopedia, updated October 12, 2021, https://www.investopedia.com/terms/a/affordable-care-act.asp.

[11] "The parts of Medicare (A, B, C, D)," Medicare Interactive, accessed October 25, 2021, https://www.medicareinteractive.org/get-answers/medicare-basics/medicare-coverage-overview/original-medicare.

[12] "Medicare: What Are Medigap Plans?" WebMD, accessed October 25, 2021, https://www.webmd.com/health-insurance/medigap#1.

[13] "Medicaid," Medicaid.gov, accessed October 25, 2021, https://www.medicaid.gov/medicaid/index.html.

[14] Jerry Ashton, Robert Goff, and Craig Antico, End Medical Debt: Curing America's $1 Trillion Unpayable Healthcare Debt (Kauai, HI: Hoku House, 2018).

[15] Ibid.

[16] "VA launches new health care options under MISSION Act," U.S. Department of Veteran Affairs, June 9, 2019, https://www.va.gov/opa/pressrel/pressrelease.cfm?id=5264.

[17] "Opinion: A new VA wait-time scandal is brewing and we have no way to know how big it is," USA Today, March 5, 2021, https://eu.usatoday.com/story/opinion/2021/03/05/veterans-affairs-wait-time-medical-appointment-trump-mcdonough-column/6820715002/.

[18] Patricia Kime, "Veterans Choice program hurting some vets' credit scores," Military Times, February 11, 2016, https://www.militarytimes.com/veterans/2016/02/11/veterans-choice-program-hurting-some-vets-credit-scores/.

Chapter One: Find The Mistakes In Your Medical Bills

[1] Ann Brenoff, "There's A Strong Chance you Are Paying For Expensive Medical Billing Mistakes," Huff Post, updated May 17, 2017, https://www.huffpost.com/entry/nearly-90-percent-of-medical-bills-contain-mistakes_n_5902146be4b0af-6d718c6e80.

[2] Anna Gorman, "Cancer's Complications: Confusing Bills, Maddening Errors and Endless Phone Calls," Kaiser Health News, February 27, 2019, https://khn.org/news/cancers-complications-confusing-bills-maddening-errors-and-endless-phone-calls/.

[3] Brenoff, "There's A Strong Chance you Are Paying For Expensive Medical Billing Mistakes."

[4] "GMA: Hidden Costs in Hospital Bills," ABC News, January 6, 2006, https://abcnews.go.com/GMA/story?id=127077&page=1.

5 "UCR (Usual, Customary, and Reasonable," HealthCare. gov, accessed October 25, 2021, https://www.healthcare.gov/ glossary/ucr-usual-customary-and-reasonable/.

6 Norma Panther, "Your Quick Guide to the Global Surgical Package," AAPC International, April 1, 2019, https://www.aapc.com/ blog/46373-your-quick-guide-to-the-global-surgical-package/.

7 "Current Procedural Terminology (CPT)," American Academy of Orthapaedic Surgeons (AAOS), accessed October 25, 2021, https://www.aaos.org/quality/coding-and-reimbursement/ current_procedural_terminology/.

8 "CPT® 99203, Under New Patient Office or Other Outpatient Services," Codify by AAPC, accessed October 25, 2021, https:// www.aapc.com/codes/cpt-codes/99203.

9 "Healthcare Common Procedure Coding System (HCPCS) Code (FFS)," ResDAC, accessed October 25, 2021, https://resdac.org/cms-data/variables/ healthcare-common-procedure-coding-system-hcpcs-code-ffs.

10 "International Classification of Diseases, Tenth Revision (ICD-10)," Centers of Disease Control and Prevention (CDC), accessed October 25, 2021, https://www.cdc.gov/nchs/icd/icd10.htm.

11 "ICD-10=CM Code R00.1," ICD.Codes, accessed October 25, 2021, https://icd.codes/icd10cm/R001.

12 "ICD-10-CM Code N39.0," ICD.Codes, accessed October 25, 2021, https://icd.codes/icd10cm/N390.

13 "What is Revenue Code?" E2E Medical Billing, November 12, 2019, https://www.e2emedicalbilling.com/blog/ what-is-revenue-code/.

14 Natalie Tornese, "Understanding Unbundling in Medical Billing," Outsource Strategies International, February 26, 2019,

https://www.outsourcestrategies.com/blog/understanding-un-bundling-medical-billing.html.

[15] "Health Insurance Portability and Accountability Act of 1996 (JIPAA)," CDC, accessed October 25, 2021, https://www.cdc.gov/phlp/publications/topic/hipaa.html.

[16] Ibid.

[17] "Managing Your Medical Bills," Kaiser Permanente, accessed October 25, 2021, https://healthy.kaiserpermanente.org/health-wellness/health-encyclopedia/he.managing-your-medi-cal-bills.abo3249.

[18] "Consequences of Coding Errors," MEREM Healthcare Solutions, accessed October 25, 2021, https://www.merem-health.com/consequence-of-medical-coding-errors/.

[19] "Observation and Discharge Policy, Professional," UnitedHealthcare, accessed October 25, 2021, https://www.uhcprovider.com/content/dam/provider/docs/public/policies/comm-reimbursement/COMM-Observation-Care-Evaluation-Mgmt-Codes-Policy.pdf.

[20] "Observation – Physician Coding FAQ," American College of Emergency Physicians, updated September 2019, https://www.acep.org/administration/reimbursement/observation---physician-coding-faq/.

[21] "CPT Codes - What are They, and How Do You Use Them?" MB-Guide, accessed October 2021, http://www.mb-guide.org/cpt-medical-billing-codes.html.

[22] Michael Sculley, "10 Common Medical Billing Mistakes That Cause Claim Denials – Part 1," Practice Suite, updated January 20, 2021, https://practicesuite.com/blog/10-common-medical-billing-mistakes-that-cause-claim-denials-part-1/.

[23] "Assistant-at-Surgery Services Policy, Professional," UnitedHealthCare, accessed October 25, 2021, https://www. uhcprovider.com/content/dam/provider/docs/public/policies/ medadv-reimbursement/MEDADV-Surgical-Assistant-Services-Policy.pdf.

[24] Elisabeth Rosenthal, "After Surgery, Surprise $117,000 Medical Bill From Doctor He Didn't Know," the New York Times, September 20, 2014, https://www.nytimes.com/2014/09/21/us/ drive-by-doctoring-surprise-medical-bills.html.

[25] "ACR Practice Parameter for Communications of Diagnostic Imaging Findings," American College of Radiology (ACR), revised 2020, https://www.acr.org/-/media/acr/files/practice-parameters/communicationdiag.pdf.

[26] Marshall Allen, "How a $175 COVID-19 Test Led to $2479 in Charges," ProPublica, August 1, 2020, https://www.propublica. org/article/how-a-covid-19-test-led-to-charges.

[27] "Ambulance CPT Codes & Modifiers (2021)," Coding Ahead, accessed October 25, 2021, https://www.codingahead.com/ ambulance-billing-guidelines-cpt-codes-html/.

[28] Ibid.

[29] Sandy Cofta, "How to Avoid Radiology Claims Denials – Medical Necessity," Healthcare Administrative Partners, accessed October 25, 2021, https://info.hapusa.com/blog-0/ how-to-avoid-radiology-claims-denials-medical-necessity.

[30] Ann Carrns, "When a Hospital Stay Is Not a Stay," the New York Times, March 18, 2014, https://www.nytimes.com/2014/03/19/ your-money/when-a-hospital-stay-is-not-a-stay.html.

[31] Emery Winter, "Yes, most hospitals are required to offer financial assistance," ABC10, updated July 22, 2021, https://www.abc10.com/article/news/verify/health-verify/

most-hospitals-required-to-offer-free-care-financial-assis-tance-for-low-income-patients/536-58a81b20-b1ef-40c0-b81c-fe45162c9303.

[32] Ashton, Goff, and Antico, End Medical Debt.

[33] Ashton, Goff, and Antico, End Medical Debt.

[34] Markian Hawryluk, "Ever Heard of a Surgical Assistant? Meet a New Boost to Your Medical Bills," Kaiser Health News, July 22, 2020, https://khn.org/news/ever-heard-of-a-surgical-assis-tant-meet-a-new-boost-to-your-medical-bills/.

[35] Ashley Lopez, "Texans Can Appeal Surprise Medical Bills, But the Process Can Be Draining," Kaiser Health News, February 13, 2019, https://khn.org/news/texans-can-appeal-surprise-med-ical-bills-but-the-process-can-be-draining/.

[36] James E. Dalen, "Only in America: Bankruptcy Due to Health Care Costs," the American Journal of Medicine 122, no. 8 (August 1, 2009), https://www.amjmed.com/article/S0002-9343(09)00525-7/fulltext.

[37] Lorie Konish, "This is the real reason most Americans file for bankruptcy," CNBC, updated February 11, 2019, https://www.cnbc.com/2019/02/11/this-is-the-real-reason-most-americans-file-for-bankruptcy.html.

[38] Christen Linke Young, Matthew Fiedler, Loren Adler, and Sobin Lee, "What is surprise billing for medical care?" Brookings, October 15, 2019, https://www.brookings.edu/policy2020/votervital/what-is-surprise-billing-for-medical-care/.

[39] Rajesh Reddy and Erin L. Duffy, "Congress Ends Surprise Billing: Implications for Prayers, Providers, and Patients," the American Journal of Managed Care 27, no. 8 (June 14, 2021), https://www.ajmc.com/view/congress-ends-surprise-billing-im-plications-for-payers-providers-and-patients.

Chapter 2: Crush Your Medical Debt

[1] Anna Almendrala, "Savvy Patient Fought for the Price She Was Quoted – and Didn't Give Up," The Union Democrat, October 29, 2020, https://www.uniondemocrat.com/lifestyle/article_7a5d08da-1a52-11eb-b1d7-9b76082df6b4.html.

[2] Ashton, Goff, and Antico, End Medical Debt.

[3] Ibid.

[4] Amy Fontinelle, "Medical Debt: What to Do When You Can't Pay," Investopedia, August 31, 2020, https://www.investopedia.com/personal-finance/medical-debt-what-do-when-you-cant-pay/.

[5] Chris Arnold, "Getting Out Of Medical Debt Can Feel Impossible. Here's How To Do It," NPR, July 14, 2020, https://www.npr.org/2019/02/14/694670747/rx-for-medical-debt.

[6] Jean Folger, "Which Retirement Funds Are Protected From Creditors?" Investopedia, May 30, 2021, https://www.investopedia.com/articles/personal-finance/040716/which-retirement-funds-are-protected-creditors.asp.

[7] "Billing and Collections – Section 501(r)(6)," Internal Revenue Service (IRS), updated August 3, 2021, https://www.irs.gov/charities-non-profits/billing-and-collections-section-501r6.

[8] "Deducting Medical Expenses for a Major Illness or Injury," Turbotax, updated October 16, 2021, https://turbotax.intuit.com/tax-tips/health-care/deducting-medical-expenses-for-a-major-illness-or-injury/L5fSkrd6C.

[9] Nancy Kerr, "Credit for Caring Act Would Provide Tax Credit to Family Caregivers," AARP, updated July 15, 2021, https://www.aarp.org/caregiving/financial-legal/info-2021/new-credit-for-caring-act.html.

[10] Phil Galewitz, "COVID-Like Cough Sent Him to ER – Where He Got a $3,278 Bill," Kaiser Health News, May 25, 2020, https://khn.org/news/covid-like-cough-covid19-symptoms-emergency-room-billing-code-surprise-medical-bill/.

[11] "COVID-19 Claims Reimbursement," Health Resources & Services Administration (HRSA), accessed October 26, 2021, https://coviduninsuredclaim.linkhealth.com.

Chapter 3: Get Help When Your Medical Debt Is Crushing You

[1] Lopez, "Texans Can Appeal Surprise Medical Bills."

[2] Ibid.

[3] Hawryluk, "Ever Heard of a Surgical Assistant?"

[4] Ashton, Goff, and Antico, End Medical Debt.

BE A MEDICAL
BILL CRUSHER!

 Get tips and strategies to save thousands of dollars and your financial life.
www.crushmedicaldebt.com

 For **special discounts** or bulk purchases, contact us at
info@crushmedicaldebt.com

 Let's continue the crushing! Join us at...
▶ **Ask a Doctor with Dr. Virgie**

CONNECT WITH OUR COMMUNITY

f **/DrVirgie**

⊙ **/therealdrvirgie**

🐦 **/therealdrvirgie**

in **/Virgie Bright Ellington, MD**

THANK YOU
FOR READING!

If **What Your Doctor Wants You to Know to Crush Medical Debt** was helpful, please leave a review on Goodreads or on the retailer site where you purchased this book and help me reach more readers like you!

Dr. Virgie

Made in the USA
Las Vegas, NV
30 March 2024

88019572R00080